CONTENTS

Types

Cracking the Curl Code

A Simple Guide to Healthy, Effortless Hair

Stephanie and
Dennis Mero

Cover Design by Kelly Wilson @vividfizz-design
Editing by Cathy and Mark Lieblich

For more information on reproducing parts of this book or publishing inquiries email crackingthecurlcode@gmail.com.

ISBN: 978-1-7342283-1-1

WHO ARE "THE CURL NINJAS"?

Stephanie (@TheCurlNinja) and Dennis (@MrCurlNinja) are professional cosmetologists who specialize in embracing natural textures of hair and educating internationally through their YouTube channel. A lot has changed since they met in 2014 (and then married in 2018). Dennis was already a seasoned cosmetologist, excelling in the industry with constant growth including receiving advanced education and teaching in salons. Stephanie was a server and aspiring freelance makeup artist with a college degree in advertising, trying to grow her experience in the beauty industry by volunteering to help with photoshoots and fashion shows. Dennis helped Stephanie understand the value of obtaining a cosmetology license and she soon enrolled in cosmetology school.

When Stephanie began her work behind the chair, she found her true calling - working with natural waves, curls, and coils, but she was still straightening her own hair. Dennis encouraged Stephanie to embrace her curls. He reassured her that, although she had hair damage, it would get better if she did so. It became easier for Stephanie when Dennis also decided to embrace his natural curls. He, too, fell in love with the art of cutting and styling natural textures and the rewards of helping people accept and love themselves on a deeper level.

In early 2019, Stephanie and Dennis started uploading educational videos to YouTube and their online presence grew quickly and significantly. They learned that the internet had its own rule book when it came to hair - one created by popular opinion rather than facts. Some of it made sense but a lot of it was false information that had gone viral. They wanted to do something about it. Together Stephanie and Dennis created a community that is focused on no-nonsense, science-based hair education. They are also raising awareness of the negative effects that social media can have on a person's self-esteem.

The emotions surrounding hair are complex and sometimes even debilitating. For this reason, Stephanie and Dennis have made it their mission to share what they believe should be common knowledge in a way that is affordable and accessible. Their next goal is to have this book translated into as many languages as possible so that it can help even more people.

In order to get this resource into the hands of those who need it as soon as possible, Stephanie and Dennis decided not to go the route of pitching the book to a publisher. They chose to self-publish and, by doing so, received no advance payment to help support them while Stephanie took several days a week to work on the book rather than seeing clients in the salon. Dennis worked overtime to keep them above water and they used weekends to read and edit out loud with each other. Low and behold - they did it! It may not be the flashiest book with the most graphics and illustrations, but it is their first book and they are proud of the information it contains. It is their truth. They began writing this book in May of 2019 and self-published in December of 2019. Stephanie and Dennis own the rights to this book and are open to talking with publishers who see a greater potential for the information contained within it.

Dedication

This book is dedicated to every family member, friend, follower, subscriber, and group member that has encouraged us along the way. Even if you were unfamiliar with us until you stumbled upon this book, just by reading it, you are also pushing us forward.

Thank you for your attention, your support, and your love. Making our way from the salon, to social media, to self-publishing has been an upwind journey with many obstacles along the way. We could not have made it this far without your support.

Now that the wind is in our sails, where to next?

All our love - Stephanie and Dennis Mero a/k/a "The Curl Ninjas"

TURN YOUR PAIN INTO POWER - STEPHANIE'S HAIR STORY

I am the only one with curly hair in my family. Before I had any control over what would happen to my hair, I was taken to a salon where they told me straightening my hair would never be an option. My parents had my hair cut extremely short after a lice breakout at school, a common occurrence in Florida. As my short cut began to grow, my stylist knew that my hair would grow out not down and so he kept the top short and let the bottom grow long. No, not a mullet. That's short in the front long in the back. Everything above my ears was cut to about 3 inches (which was only about 1 inch when curly and was the only way I could wear it) and everything below my ears touched my shoulders or longer. My hairstyle was more than a decade outdated. I stood out from my peers in elementary and middle school, and not in a good way.

Every single day I was reminded of that and there was nothing I could do about it at the time.

I became frustrated with the feeling of hopelessness I would get after every salon appointment, always leaving with that same haircut. I stopped getting it cut and in 8th grade my life changed forever: those short top layers fit into a hair tie. I will never forget that moment, wandering into my parents' bathroom after the epiphany that maybe the top of my hair could be pulled migraine-level-tight into a tiny ponytail-poof, going into my mother's drawer, finding an elastic hair band there, reaching up for my hair, and pulling with all my might to bring it together and tie it. It worked. I looked at myself in the mirror. I looked normal. The significance of that moment in my life cannot be overstated. Up until that point, I believed I would look exactly the same forever and that no one would ever look past my hair.

Suddenly I was no longer a walking target for bullies, and just in time for high school and the rise of social media. I most likely would not have been posting many photos of myself online with that haircut but I can only imagine what the anonymous bullies of the internet would have said about it if I did. You would not believe the things people would say right to my face. But now, hidden away in a half-up half-down hairstyle, the top of my hair could grow out. When straightening treatments started to become popular, I went back to the salon I had abandoned so I could be their guinea-pig. It had been enough time of growing out the top of my hair so that when it was straight I had short layers. The treatment didn't make my hair completely straight and so the flat iron became an extension of my right arm. High school, college, and even cosmetology school passed by without feeling confident enough to stop straightening my hair.

When I started working at my first salon, I was introduced to product for curly hair and I let my hair fully air dry, curly, for the first time in 12 years. My hair was more like fried squiggles than curls. When my husband (then boyfriend) Dennis saw me, he knew it had a long way to go but he reassured me that it would only get better. It made me feel better, but it didn't take away the horrible memories connected to my curly hair. I decided I would give it a try but I didn't want to just spring my new look on people. I needed to test the waters first so I grabbed my phone and took a selfie (okay, maybe more than one selfie) until I had one that I felt okay about. When I posted it, I was met with mixed responses which made it even harder. Unfortunately, people who have never been made fun of for their hair or had to hide their hair to meet society's standards of beauty or professionalism do not understand how much it hurts when someone tells you that they like your hair better straight.

I did not feel confident. I did not want to go out. I did not want to put any more photos on social media. I didn't cave in to those feelings and straighten my hair that day but there were plenty of times that I did before completely giving it up because, you know what? It was hard to overcome the filter that had formed over my eyes from the years and years of being told that straight hair is better and being treated differently because my hair was curly. I now know how to feel beautiful with curly hair, but for the first few months of my hair transition, I had days where I just didn't have the confidence to wear it curly. I straightened it those days, and whether or not it actually looked better to anyone but me, it made me feel better at the time.

I didn't cut off all of my old damaged hair until April 2018, a week after I married Dennis. I gave up heat-styling completely after that. However, the obstacles did not end there. Growing out a one-inch curly haircut was hard. There were so many phases in which my hair didn't feel like me.

I would even avoid certain outfits because I felt that my hair didn't "go" with them.

Specializing professionally in cutting and caring for waves, curls, and coils helped me through my own grow-out. There is so much comfort in knowing that you are not alone with something you are experiencing. Every day I was helping other women gain the confidence to rock their hair even if it meant going through a tough transition. I thank every single client who has sat in my chair because you all have truly transformed me and I would not be where I am or who I am if you had not trusted me and been vulnerable with me.

It has been 18 months since that first chop and I just recently cut my hair even shorter than the first time. The circumstances are very different (you will learn more about this later in the book if you don't already know) but the feeling is the same. I have to find other ways to feel confident. When I do not have my curls, I am forced to realize that I am not my hair.

We are not the things that we did not ask for and that we cannot change. We are not our bodies or what they do or do not naturally produce. We are the things we think, feel and do. We are the things we create. We are love, sadness, hope, fear, and happiness. We are good. We are worthy. We are powerful. Unlike our hair - we can heal even if we break. Hardships do not damage us - they strengthen us. There will be days that your hair feels like a burden. I am here to tell you that the only way to avoid that feeling entirely is to let go. Accept that no matter how much you understand your hair, you will have days when things do not go as planned. We cannot master something that is always changing. The key is not to call any days "bad hair days".

There is no bad hair; there is only hair that does not look the way you want it to. That being said, I hope this book and the other resources I plan to share in the future will give you as much power as possible to get what you want every day. Healthy hair is an important piece of a more low-maintenance lifestyle. I only worry about how much power over our self-esteem we give to something we cannot completely control. I truly hope this book will empower you to love your hair, no matter how it is or how it changes, and let go of any desire to reach a standard other than your own. Just in case you have not heard it or felt it lately - you are strong and you are beautiful, just as you are.

INTRODUCTION: WAVES, CURLS, AND COILS, OH MY!

When did caring for and styling hair in its natural state get so complicated? Isn't part of the appeal to be able to do *less*? Yet for some reason most of the people we speak to on our social media platforms are spending more time, money, and energy on their hair than they ever did when they were forcing it straight. An overload of products and information has caused mass confusion when it comes to hair care and styling. It's time for some clarity.

First and foremost: Hair is hair. You do not need to know if your hair is straight, wavy, curly, extra-curly, zig zag patterned or any other of the patterns that have been charted in an attempt to segregate hair types based on their shape. It is not important when it comes to choosing products and it is not important when it comes to choosing styling techniques.

It is not true that the tighter a curl pattern is, the drier it is. Some people have hair that is prone to dryness just like some people have skin that is prone to dryness. Just like skin tone does not cause dry skin - the shape of the hair strand does not cause dry hair. There may be a *correlation* between certain hair types and dryness but the hair type is not the *cause.*

Moisture comes from only one thing: *water*. Hair needs water - not product. It can seem like it needs product when it is dry or damaged and using product makes it feel and look better. A lot of products contain water or help trap water in the hair. However, a substance cannot provide moisture without the presence of water and hair should not need the help of products to retain moisture. A healthy hair strand lets in moisture and locks moisture in, even once it has fully dried.

The hair strand stops functioning properly when it doesn't receive *or* retain the water it needs. The health and function of hair is also compromised when certain behaviors or environmental factors cause damage to the hair strand. Dryness and damage are ailments most of us are familiar with but how they occur and how to treat them is not common knowledge. Once you have understood the information in this book, you will know how to identify the current condition of your hair, help it become healthy if it is not, and, most importantly, prevent it from becoming unhealthy again.

There is one thing we can not teach you: *patience.* The hardest part of reaching your goal for your hair, whether it be health or length, will be waiting to get there. However, if you fully commit to your new routine and follow the guidelines in this book, you will reach your goals as quickly as humanly possible. You might even find that you enjoy the journey. That is our hope for you and one of our primary purposes for writing this book.

This book is not a rule book. What you do or don't do to your hair is your choice and we are not here to judge you or scold you. It's your hair and we want you to own it. If this is the first "formal" hair education you are receiving, we recommend reading this book from beginning to end. If you are already knowledgeable about a lot of topics we cover, or if you are looking to find something that you forgot, you can use the book as a reference and utilize the table of contents to jump to specific topics. Think of it as having your own pocket-hair-professional.

This book contains some ideas that may surprise you and other ideas that you may already be familiar with. It is not segmented by gender, ethnicity, or wave and curl patterns, because it does not need to be. It is a book about hair science, how to make informed decisions for your hair, and tips for styling it in its natural state. With this information under your belt, you may find there is more bounce to your strands than you thought possible. Healthy hair plus the right products for your unique hair needs (and wants) will always reveal the most shape. So, how do you know if your hair is healthy or not? What do you do if it isn't? If it is, then how do you prevent it from becoming unhealthy? We are going to walk you through all of that, but first, we want you to understand how the hair strand works and learn some key terms that will pop up throughout the book.

CHAPTER 1: ANATOMY OF HAIR

As more and more misinformation circulates online, science-based knowledge is the only way to escape the massive game of telephone that is social media idea-sharing. Understanding the parts of the hair strand, their purposes, and their functions is key to understanding hair like a professional. When you understand how the hair strand works, it will be easier to understand when it is not working properly.

Follicle Structure & Hair Strand

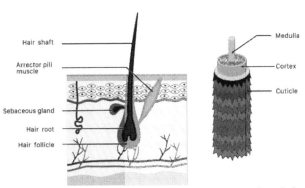

The arrector pili muscle connects to the follicle but is not part of the hair strand or hair follicle. Its contraction is why hair can seem to "stand up" when you have chills. The medulla is the third, innermost structure of some hair strands. It is not currently known if the medulla serves any purpose. Not all hair contains a medulla and it is not necessary to hair health to possess one.

THE FOLLICLE

Although technically not a part of the hair strand, it is important to understand the follicle because it is the womb of the hair strand. Inside the follicle, the hair strand is formed and coated with a thin layer of sebum, our natural protective oils. The shape of the follicle and the angle at which the hair strand leaves the follicle and extends beyond the scalp both play a part in determining the shape of the hair strand (straight, wavy, curly, etc.).

The cells that make up the hair strand are only alive while the hair is still inside the follicle. Only new hair that is being formed inside the follicle can be affected by hormones, diet, and anything else internal. For example, a change in diet can affect the hair forming in the follicle but it will not have any impact on the hair that has already left the follicle. The same applies in the reverse situation. Nothing you do to the hair that is past the follicle will affect the new hair forming inside of it.

SEBACEOUS GLANDS AND SEBUM

Inside the follicle, the hair strand receives a protective layer of natural oils, known as sebum, from the sebaceous glands. Sebaceous glands are located under the skin and connect to the follicle. Sebum serves the purpose of keeping the hair and scalp healthy by maintaining pH balance on the surface of the skin and hair and acting as a natural guard against bacteria. Sebum is slightly acidic, with a pH between 4.5 and 6.5. It is important for our skin and hair products to stay within that pH range so that the sebum layer is not broken down.

Without the layer of sebum on our skin we can develop dandruff, acne, and other skin disorders. Luckily our skin replenishes sebum quickly. However, it is much more challenging for hair strands to receive new sebum from beneath the skin. If you have ever had extremely dry hair, you may have noticed that the underneath layer was much healthier. That is because the hair underneath touches the surface of our skin and borrows sebum from it. For someone with healthy hair, that underneath layer may look looser because of the weight of the sebum it absorbed from the skin. All it needs is a stronger cleanse to help those strands bounce back up.

Underneath the layer of sebum is the actual surface of the hair strand. The surface of the hair strand is much more acidic. Without the sebum layer increasing the pH of the hair strand, the cuticle will close up too tightly, making it very difficult to penetrate with water and hair product.

THE CUTICLE

The cuticle is the outermost layer of the hair strand. It is composed of shingle-like layers that overlap, like on a roof. However, unlike shingles which are set in place, the layers of a normal, healthy cuticle lift and lower to let in moisture and lock it in. Its purpose is to protect from dryness and damage. The condition of the cuticle is the most important factor in determining hair health and needs.

A healthy cuticle is slightly raised in its resting position (when hair is dry) in order to allow water to seep through and hydrate the hair. It softens and lifts as water absorbs into the strand and lowers back down as water leaves the hair strand. It will dry once excess water is released and it is back in its resting position. The condition of the cuticle impacts the porosity of the hair strand, which we will discuss later.

THE CORTEX

The cortex contains chains of keratin proteins linked together by hydrogen and disulfide bonds that help keep the hair strong and the shape of the strands (wave or curl pattern) intact. Salt bonds and sugar bonds which link to the amino acids of the hair strand have a lesser impact on the strength and structure of the hair. The cortex also contains melanin that determines the color of the hair. Just like our internal organs and our skin, the cortex needs to absorb and retain moisture to be healthy. It also needs the bonds between proteins kept strong.

Like a sponge, the cortex absorbs moisture. Absorption of water that passes through the gaps between cuticle layers causes the cortex to swell, become heavier with water weight, and push open the cuticle further. However, unlike a sponge, the cortex has the cuticle which acts as a gateway that raises and lowers to let it receive and retain moisture.

Imagine putting a wet sponge into a sealed container versus leaving it out on the counter, exposed to the air. The exposed sponge is going to dry out completely, becoming stiff and weak. A healthy cuticle will keep the cortex from drying out completely. Although the cortex holds the most important parts of the hair strand, cuticle function is what will determine its overall health.

CHAPTER 2: HAIR TERMINOLOGY

There is a lot of language around hair that can be confusing. We felt that this section was important in order to break down some of the words that describe hair in a way that clears up some common misconceptions and is easy to understand.

Hair Density

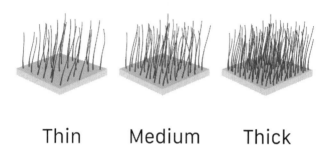

Thin   Medium   Thick

TEXTURE AND DENSITY

Texture and density are often confused with each other but they are very different descriptors when it comes to hair. The texture of our hair is the diameter, or thickness, of an individual strand. There are three commonly used categories: fine, medium, and coarse. Density is the ratio of hair strands per square inch of scalp. Density also has three common categories: thin (low), medium, and thick (high).

The "finger-roll test" is the easiest way to determine hair texture. Take a strand of hair (you can keep it attached to your scalp) and roll it between your two fingers. For fine hair you should not be able to feel the hair strand. If you can faintly feel the strand, it can be considered medium. Coarse hair, which has the largest diameter, can be easily felt using this "finger-roll test".

The easiest way to determine your density is to part your hair all the way to the scalp. If you can easily see almost as much scalp as hair strands then your density in that area of your hair would be described as thin, or low. If you can see a little bit of scalp but mostly hair then it could be described as medium. Thick hair, or high-density hair, will reveal almost no visible scalp when you part your hair.

Density and texture will not be uniform throughout your scalp and hair. However, there are some variances that most humans share. The hairline that runs across the border of the forehead, behind the ears, and along the base of the neck, tends to be a finer texture and lower density are called "weak" areas of the hair.

Medium and coarse textures do not have any special considerations to take into account when it comes to choosing products. However, fine hair cannot hold as much styling product as medium and coarse hair can, so not as much product is needed. Fine hair can also be easily weighed down. Be mindful of how much styling product you use if you have fine hair and limit the use of leave-in conditioners which tend to be heavy and will not leave room for styling product.

ELASTICITY

The elasticity of hair is its ability to re-turn back to its original state after being stretched. Although healthy hair is more elastic when it is wet than when it is dry, it is not stronger when it is wet. When hair is wet it can easily over-stretch and cause breakage of the hair strand.

There is no accurate test for elasticity that you can perform at home. Pulling a strand of hair and seeing how much it bounces back is an extremely biased experiment. Physical strength varies so greatly among humans that this test cannot provide an objectively accurate result. Just know that healthy hair will be more elastic than un-healthy hair, so keeping your hair healthy makes it more resilient.

PH OF HAIR

The pH scale is used to describe the acidity, neutrality, or alkalinity of a substance. Water is supposed to be a neutral 7. Everything below 7 is acidic and anything above 7 is alkaline. Products with a pH higher than 7 will raise the cuticle. For example, relaxers and permanent hair color processes use alkalinity to keep the cuticle open in order to make a physical change inside the hair strand. As long as damage does not occur, the cuticle will lower back down after the change is made. Acidic substances, such as apple cider vinegar or citrus juices, will actively lower the cuticle. Hair products you use at home should have a pH within the same range as healthy hair and skin, which is somewhere between 4.5-6.5.

NORMAL POROSITY

The porosity of a substance is the size of its openings relative to the total volume of the substance. All porous substances have openings which allow absorption. Sponges, wood, and rocks are all porous materials. However, they differ in porosity levels. A sponge is more porous than wood and wood is more porous than rock.

Hair porosity is measured differently than most porous materials because the cortex is what absorbs moisture (and therefore is porous) but the hair strand also has a cuticle that acts as a gateway. Unlike sponges, wood, and rocks which have a more constant porosity - the porosity of hair can frequently change because of the fluctuating position of the cuticle.

A "normal" porosity means that the cuticle functions as it is naturally supposed to. Its lowest position should be slightly raised, creating tiny gaps for water to flow through so the hair can absorb moisture. This "resting" position varies and that is why normal porosity is such a big spectrum. Normal porosity can range from low-normal (LNP) to high-normal (HNP). A medium-normal porosity (MNP) falls somewhere in-between. It is important to recognize that normal porosity is not a set amount where you could measure your cuticle opening and determine your porosity.

The type of porosity fluctuates naturally due to behavioral and environmental factors. However, if you understand the characteristics of each porosity type, then you can identify which type your hair most closely falls into. How the hair strand reacts to water is the main indicator of porosity type.

Cuticle Condition & Porosity

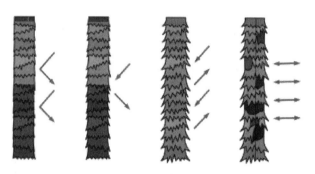

| Low | Normal | High | Destroyed |

This diagram uses arrows to show how water enters and exits the hair strand for each porosity type. For low, the water bounces off the outside of the cuticle layers, never penetrating the hair strand. For normal, the water enters and exits at a natural pace. For high, water goes in and out of the hair strand, but more moisture is lost than normal. For destroyed, the water enters and exits freely, with no resistance from the cuticle layer, and all moisture is released when dry.

ABNORMAL POROSITY

When the cuticle does not lower enough to seal in moisture, it is called high porosity (HP). High porosity hair accepts water but does not retain a healthy, normal amount. The result is that it loses more moisture than it should when it dries. This porosity type can be caused by minor damage to the cuticle layer or an increase in the pH of the surface of the hair. When caused by damage, it can sometimes be improved with protein and conditioning treatments. When it is caused by a pH imbalance it can be improved with acidic rinses, such as apple cider vinegar, or looking for hair products with a pH that is close to the lower end of normal pH.

Some people believe that an overabundance of moisture over time can cause the cuticle to become "tired." This condition, termed "hygral fatigue", is not something we have seen before and so we can not speak to its validity. Hair loves moisture and although using too much water can cause hair to look unsatisfactory when styled, it is hard for us to believe that too much moisture would cause a "lazy cuticle" to the point of causing high porosity.

If high porosity hair is left untreated, the cuticle can easily become destroyed and further damage to the hair strand is more likely to occur. Destroyed high porosity (DHP) is caused by extreme damage to the cuticle layer. Some of the cuticle layer will have peeled off or frayed open, leaving the cortex permanently exposed. Destroyed high porosity hair accepts water but then quickly releases all of it, leaving it extremely dry, weak and difficult to manage. It cannot be repaired, but there are ways to maintain it until it is cut off. Protein and conditioning treatments will help improve the look and feel of hair with this porosity type. Cream-based styling products and leave-in conditioners are also helpful to keep the hair soft once it dries.

They can also improve the appearance and feel of high porosity hair.

The third type of abnormal porosity is low porosity (LP). Low porosity can be caused by buildup of substances that block water, products that are too acidic, and loss of sebum due to the use of harsh cleansers. Product buildup occurs the most with non-water-soluble ingredients being used by people who also use very gentle cleansers that do not break them down. Once buildup is removed, if the cuticle is still refusing to open, warm water can help raise it to increase absorption. When the cortex starts getting the water it needs along with the continued use of gentle cleansers with a balanced pH, low porosity hair can increase to a normal porosity and stay that way.

CHARACTERISTICS OF POROSITY TYPES

- **Low Porosity (LP)**: a closed cuticle repels water and product; water tends to bead and pool in pockets outside the hair; dry hair strand feels smooth between fingers; dull appearance
- **Low-Normal Porosity (LNP)**: a tight cuticle opening slowly takes in water but does become fully wet; retains moisture when it dries; gains very little water weight when wet, shiny when dry
- **Medium-Normal Porosity (MNP)**: a slightly raised cuticle readily accepts water but not much excess; hair is shiny when dry
- **High-Normal Porosity (HNP)**: a more-raised cuticle rapidly absorbs water in excess; the cuticle traps excess water causing hair to be very heavy when wet and prone to tangling; retains moisture once dry; shiny when dry

- **High Porosity (HP)**: an overly-raised cuticle releases water; tangles profusely when wet and when dry; requires styling product to retain moisture; hair strand feels rigid when dry
- **Destroyed High Porosity (DHP)**: a cuticle that has frayed or peeled off releases water and product; tangles profusely when wet and when dry; requires styling product to retain moisture; can be managed with products but not repaired to normal function

CHAPTER 3: TRANSITIONING AND PREVENTING DAMAGED HAIR

If you have assessed the condition of your cuticle and determined that your hair is not damaged, you can skip to the next section, "Detangling", which is the beginning of our information regarding common causes of damage and breakage. Prevention of future damage is just as important as treating current damage, so that information is useful for everyone who has hair, no matter what current condition it is in.

If you have diagnosed some or all of your

hair as destroyed high porosity, then you now understand that it will eventually need to be cut off in order to remove all damage from your hair. However, *when* it is cut off is entirely up to you. There is more than one way to go through the process of removing severely damaged hair. We suggest cutting your damage off completely only once your new, healthy hair is at a length you are comfortable with. For some people that might be just an inch or less and for others it might be waiting until it is at their shoulders or longer. There is no right or wrong decision. The choice is *yours* alone.

Don't let anyone bully you into thinking you have to cut off your damaged hair. Decisions regarding your hair belong to you and the condition and appearance of your hair is really no one else's business. When you are ready to cut it, you will, but don't feel bad if you just can't prioritize hair health over length yet. Just like we have been brainwashed to believe straight hair is ideal, the same thing goes for long hair for women. It is not fair but just because it isn't fair doesn't mean it isn't true. Until physical standards based on gender become obsolete, that is how it will be.

Even as society gets closer to accepting different ideas of beauty, our minds will not always be ready to agree. We hope this book will help increase your confidence to a point where you can see yourself as beautiful with your hair at any length. Remember, it will grow. When we have clients decide to cut their hair shorter than their goal length because they do not want to deal with the damage anymore, we like to say, "If you can live with it today, you can love it forever." If you are currently just "living with" your hair, we hope this book will help you love it much sooner.

If you want to maintain your length while you grow out healthy hair then you can leave it alone until your new hair is long enough or cut the damage off in phases. If your healthy hair is a lot curlier than your damaged hair, holding on to damage as it grows can be a challenge. You can try using the styling techniques for elongation described in the styling portion of this book to make your healthy hair look more like the curl pattern of the damaged hair. This will help balance the appearance as it grows out. Attempting to make your damaged hair curl up as much as the new healthy hair will be a greater challenge.

Once all of your hair is healthy (or if it already is), and in order to make sure it stays healthy, you need to understand the common causes of damage and breakage. If optimal hair health is your top priority, then you need to avoid potential causes of damage and breakage completely. Be wary that damage to hair by any of these behaviors and processes can result in a loss of wave or curl pattern. However, wearing your hair in one style all the time can be boring, and that is why we are not going to tell you not to do anything that might damage your hair or scold you if you do. Instead, we will educate you on the causes and how to best prevent damage without total abstinence from damaging behaviors.

DETANGLING

We commonly determine ease of detangling by assessing how quickly our detangling tool, whether it is a comb, brush, or fingers, makes it through our hair without resistance. Water and conditioner make our hair feel soft and so detangling wet hair seems easier. However, as we mentioned in our section on elasticity, wet hair is weaker than dry hair. When hair is wet it can break so easily that you do not hear a "snap" the way you would if it broke while dry.

When we do not know hair is breaking, we won't be as gentle with our detangling and so we will get through the knots faster. However, getting through them is not the same as undoing them. Breaking off the hairs around a knot until it comes out is what generally happens during wet-detangling and that is why it is common to see so much hair come out in the shower without a corresponding noticeable loss of density at the scalp.

Not only does wet-detangling cause breakage, it can also damage the hair strands. When the cuticle is raised, it is at greater risk of becoming damaged from the friction caused by brushing or combing. If we don't do our detangling when our hair is wet, when should we do so?

(Re-)Introducing: dry-detangling. Dry-detangling became unpopular in the wavy and curly hair community because of how "poofy" it causes hair to be. Someone with straight hair can detangle and smooth their hair while it is dry without causing frizz but most people with straight hair wet-detangle anyway. Why? Because of marketing and the tools and products that suggest it should be done wet. It has become rare to see someone with long, thick, healthy straight hair that doesn't involve extensions. As hair gets longer and has been wet-brushed a lot, the amount of breakage increases until finally it is like the hair won't grow past a certain length, or the last few inches become thin and weak.

Dry-detangling is the safest way to smooth hair and remove knots for all hair types. Using your fingers or even a wide tooth comb to detangle dry hair may be more time consuming but that is because you are more likely to be gentle on your hair and take the time to really undo a knot so that you don't hear the snapping of strands. You feel a greater resistance because the hair is stronger. Using your fingers will allow you to spread out and massage a tangle to actually undo it without causing breakage. No comb or brush has the mechanism that your fingers do to massage out knots and that is why we always recommend finger-detangling. To make it easier, you can use a product on your hands that creates slip, such as conditioner, without fully wetting your hair.

We believe that getting as many knots out as possible while your hair is dry is the best technique to use for detangling *only if* hair health and minimum breakage are a priority over time spent detangling. That is up to you. You would use this technique before wetting your hair in the shower so don't stress about how it looks after you have dry-detangled. If your hair re-tangles when it gets wet, then gently smooth it out with your hands using conditioner. It should be significantly less tangled than if you did not dry-detangle beforehand.

We recognize that there are a plethora of tools on the market for detangling and styling wet hair. Most people are willing to spend money to make detangling and styling quicker and easier or to achieve a more desirable result. If the tool provides some benefit that is more valuable to you than avoiding breakage and damage as much as possible, there is nothing wrong with that. We only want you to understand the risks associated with wet-brushing and combing so you can make an informed decision.

A challenge many people face in detangling is single strand knots or "fairy knots". First and foremost, single strand knots are not some type of disease of the hair. They happen with curly hair and cutting them off will not make them go away. If you want your hair to grow long, we do not suggest cutting knots off that are not on the very ends of your hair. Some of your single strand knots could have actually involved other strands at some point. When hair breaks off around a knot instead of detangling it, the result will be a tiny knot left on a single hair strand. Using our detangling tips can help prevent this from happening.

HIGH-HEAT STYLING

High-quality heat protectants will make a huge difference when heat-styling. Heat protectants create a barrier between your hair strands and the heat source. Most protect up to 400 degrees fahrenheit, so your hot tool should never be set higher than that. The best heat protectants will contain water-soluble silicones which coat the hair strand and protect it.

Flat irons are the most direct and dangerous source of heat. Always make sure that your hair is completely dry before using a flat iron, wand or curling iron on it. A diffuser is a great option for styling without causing heat damage. It is an attachment that replaces the nozzle of the blowdryer and distributes the air flow and the heat so that it is less direct. We suggest using the dryer on a medium heat setting and not leaving the diffuser in one spot for more than 10 seconds. We do not believe that heat protectants are needed for diffusing in this manner, but you are welcome to use one if you have one that you like.

Try not to overlap hair that is already straight and only retouch hair that has curled back up. Protecting your hair overnight with a silk or satin scarf or other method that will help your style stay intact will avoid the need for touch-ups. Plan to do a mask for moisture before your next wash. Cleansing can stress out your hair so prepping with extra moisture will help relieve that stress. You can try misting your hair until it is damp and applying a mask or conditioner for 20-30 minutes and using a plastic cap to trap in warmth from your head before washing. Rinse and follow up with your usual cleanser and conditioner.

Heat-Styling Tip - Danielle Carrington @deecarrington

"When my clients choose to wear their hair straight on occasion, I like to give them a conditioning treatment before the blow-dry. I al-

ways apply a professional heat protectant before blow-drying. If I go in with the iron to smooth the hair further, I make sure not to pass over the hair multiple times."

PROFESSIONAL COLOR SERVICES

Damage and breakage can happen during color processing if products that are highly alkaline like lightener or high-ammonia dyes are left on for too long or used with heat and not monitored properly. Heat influences the amount of lift we can achieve with color or lightener, the professional term for bleach, because it speeds up the chemical reaction. Because of this, it is more risky to lighten hair using heat than without it.

There are several sources of heat that may be used, either intentionally or unintentionally. There are the obvious sources, such as hood dryers or heat lamps. However, foil also conducts heat. When doing foil highlights, the stylist should be paying attention and checking the foils occasionally, especially if they are using an additional heat source on top of the foil. Our scalps are another source of heat. "Hot roots" occur when the heat from the scalp increases the chemical process at the root area, causing the roots to lift to a lighter color than the rest of the hair.

An alternative to using lightener is called high-lift color. It is more gentle on hair but it has limits. High-lift color cannot remove other artificial color from the hair, so it is only an option if the hair has never been colored before. The underlying pigment of hair is warm and that is what will be revealed when dark hair is lightened using high-lift color, even if it has never been colored before. Do not expect a neutral or cool result when using high-lift on dark hair. Using lightener is the most effective way to remove pigment and guarantee a more than a few levels of lift, but it can also be the most damaging when it comes to professional color services if not performed carefully.

How chemically-processed hair is cared for at home is extremely important. A stylist can take measures to protect your hair in the salon, but they can't control your home care. It is the stylist's job to educate you on how to take care of your hair at home but it is your responsibility to follow through on those instructions. Hair is always more vulnerable to further damage after color processing. High-quality products are important for maintaining the color and condition of the hair. Gentle cleansing and occasional protein and conditioning treatments will help treat damage and prevent breakage.

Always be completely honest with the stylist performing the color service and give them a full list of chemical services done in the past. Just because you can no longer see color or the effects of another chemical service when you look at your hair does not mean it is gone. If you are not sure if the hair on your head is still processed or if it has been cut off, the stylist can test for existing color by doing a strand test. It is important to be certain that nothing is going to interfere with your results before undergoing the often long and expensive process of doing a big color change. For all new color services, always do a patch test on your skin first to make sure you do not have an adverse reaction to the product. When going lighter in color, we recommend being patient. Slow and steady will win the race to healthy hair.

We suggest waiting at least eight weeks between appointments if you are going to be overlapping hair that has already been color processed. This will give the hair strands time to recover. The safest way to color hair is to go darker using semi-permanent hair dye, also referred to as no-lift or deposit-only. This type of hair dye will tint the cuticle but not penetrate the hair strand into the cortex. It is not possible to go lighter in color using a semi-permanent dye. Going darker is generally safer than going lighter, except in the case of non-professional color services, as explained in the next section.

Coloring Tip for Stylists - Leysa Carillo @leysahairandmakeup

"Toning blondes with permanent color will provide a more balanced look if the hair has multiple porosities. It will lift the hair, deposit the tone and seal the cuticle. I like to tone with permanent because the lifting action allows you to take the color a little bit lighter without over-lifting with lightener and causing damage. Toning with permanent color will also make the color last longer."

NON-PROFESSIONAL COLOR

Some hair dyes can be bought from drug stores and non-professional beauty suppliers without a cosmetology license. Coloring your hair with non-professional product can cause extreme damage. No matter whether your goal is lighter or darker color, these dyes penetrate the hair strands aggressively, often causing irreversible damage to the hair strand.

"Box-dyes" are those you see at drugstores and supermarkets. They are designed to guarantee the color on the box no matter what the starting color of the hair is. They use extremely harsh chemicals to ensure the result. This damage can occur even when going darker. The box does not know the starting shade because it cannot do a consultation first the way that a professional can. The ingredients in the box dye will lift your hair even if your goal is darker than your starting shade, just in case your starting color was darker.

There are other non-professional dyes that can be just as harmful as box dyes. They are sold at beauty supply stores that do not require a license to purchase, but do require measurement and mixing of the product. Measuring and mixing the product gives the illusion of a professional service. However, the negative impact on the hair is often the same.

Henna dyes are a popular product because they are perceived to be natural. Henna dyes purchased anywhere that does not require a professional license can be harmful to our hair and our skin because they contain metallic salts. There are professional-grade dyes that use henna. As long as they have purified the henna to remove the metallic salts, these products should be a safe color alternative.

PERMANENT SMOOTHING AND WAVING TREATMENTS

Smoothing treatments or relaxers and permanent waving treatments or perms can be performed at salons to change the physical shape of the hair. These treatments use highly alkaline ingredients to keep the cuticle open so that a physical change can occur inside the cortex. The disulfide bonds that hold the keratin protein chains together are broken so that the shape of the strand can be permanently re-formed in the new shape.

Chemical treatments that change the shape of the hair can be extremely damaging to the hair and scalp. Frequent application of these chemicals to the scalp can damage the follicles and cause premature hair loss. Damage to the hair strands will make them more porous and more susceptible to further damage and breakage. After a chemical treatment, we suggest avoiding heat-styling and color processing to minimize the risk of further damage or breakage.

SUN, SALTWATER, AND CHLORINE

The sun can hurt our hair just like it does our skin. The best way to protect your hair from UV light is to cover it, whether it is with a hat, a scarf, or an umbrella. Most sunscreens for skin are formulated to be resistant to water and contain chemicals that are not ideal for use in hair. Using sunscreen on your hair may protect it from the UV light but could cause other issues like buildup or dryness. There are hair products formulated with UV protection that would be preferable to using sunscreen on hair.

As we mentioned earlier in the book, hair is more vulnerable to damage when it is wet. When the hair is wet and the cuticle is open, it is also more exposed to UV light. Frequent, prolonged exposure to sunlight with wet hair will eventually cause the hair to lighten in color and lose moisture.

After taking a dip in the pool, lake, spring, or ocean or even using the poolside shower, remove as much water from your hair as possible by squeezing with your hands and then gently again with a towel. This will help the cuticle lower and protect the hair. You can also protect it with a hat or other hair covering.

Straw hats with holes will still permit light to come through, so we suggest using a covering that is tightly woven. Saltwater and chlorine can dry out your hair which can increase your risk of breakage. If you first rinse your hair with fresh water until it is fully wet, this can slightly decrease the amount of chlorine or saltwater that is absorbed in a short period of submersion. However, it will not prevent absorption completely.

Cleansing and conditioning your hair as soon as possible after exposure to salt-water or chlorine is the best way to keep harmful substances from lingering. We believe the only way to completely protect hair from being penetrated by salt or chlorine is to stay above water, but healthy hair can handle a little chlorine or saltwater on occasion. Do not stop living your life because of your hair. Just make sure to give it some extra love and care before and after.

HIGH-TENSION HAIRSTYLES

Braids, ponytails, and buns are fun and often convenient alternatives to wearing your hair down but they can come at a cost. Tight hairstyles that create tension on strands can cause breakage to the hair and damage the follicle. Styling your hair in a loose, relaxed way that puts minimum tension on the hair and scalp is the safest way to style hair besides wearing it down. A wide non-elastic headband is a useful tool when pulling your hair back away from your face because it will do a lot of the work for the hair-tie, laying the hair down against the scalp without needing a lot of tension. The hairline is the most fragile part of the hair and a non-elastic headband can help protect it from breakage and follicle damage.

There are many types of hair-ties on the market. Now there is everything from a standard elastic to plastic, accordion-like devices. Elastic hair ties tend to snag hair so we suggest avoiding them completely. Even with other "safer" elastic-free hairties, you should still be mindful of your technique as you wrap them around your hair. One loop is best but that is not enough tension for most people, especially during exercise or sports. When doing multiple wrap-arounds with the hair-tie, make sure not to grab individual hairs in the wrapping process and cause them to tangle up with the hair-tie. Remove the hair-tie slowly and gently, one loop at a time. Styling clips can also cause breakage. We suggest avoiding metal clips, especially those with ridges or "teeth". A plastic clip with no teeth is the safest way to pin your hair into place without causing breakage. Always be careful when removing clips from your hair.

Braided styles, whether they are for the purpose of seeing the braids or as a base for hair extensions or an installed wig, can create extreme tension on the hair and scalp if the braids are very tight. This tension over time can cause breakage of hair strands and irreparable damage to follicles. Always go to a braider who will be mindful of what your hair and scalp will look like when the braids are taken out. A consultation with a professional braider should help determine if your hair is a good candidate for the style you want. You should also be educated on proper home care for the style.

SLEEPING HABITS

Being mindful of what happens to your hair when you sleep can help reduce damage and preserve your hairstyle so it can be enjoyed the next day with minimal refreshing needed. Who wouldn't love to "wake up and go"? If only we could all sleep hanging from the ceiling like bats and wake up with definition and volume.

Satin and silk pillowcases and hair coverings are a popular way to reduce friction that can cause damage and disrupt your hairstyle. One or the other is often sufficient for someone who is a sound sleeper. However, for maximum protection, we suggest using both a silk pillowcase and a silk hair covering such as a scarf, bonnet, or wrap. Some hairstyles will look better in the morning after coming out of a hair covering and others will look better without it. It depends on the length and texture so figure out what works best for you.

Some people like to do overnight treatments. Keep in mind that it is not healthy for your scalp to go to sleep with your hair covered in a cap or any other cover if it is wet or damp. Your head is warm and the warm moisture on your scalp will create a natural place for bacteria to grow. Taking care of your scalp is crucial to a healthy head of hair. We will go further into scalp care next.

CHAPTER 4: SCALP HEALTH

We are not dermatologists, but we will share what we know from our experience and education about a healthy scalp and how it affects our hair. A healthy scalp is crucial for the growth of healthy hair; that we know for sure. The scalp is coated in sebum that moisturizes and protects. Without its protective layer of sebum, the scalp can form bacteria that results in dandruff and other skin conditions such as acne and rosacea. Loss of natural oils can also cause dry scalp. Both dandruff and dry scalp produce flakes, but dry scalp flakes are white while dandruff flakes are more yellow in color.

As much as we do not want to strip

away our natural oils, we also should not let them build up. Buildup from sebum, products, and hard water can all cause a decrease in scalp health. Washing with a clarifying shampoo can help break down buildup. However, if your hair is prone to dryness, you should focus your clarifying cleansers only on the scalp area. Warm water can also help break down buildup.

NORMAL VS. ABNORMAL SHEDDING

We mentioned earlier that shedding occurs from the scalp while breakage happens down the hair strand. Shedding is natural and unavoidable for all humans as our follicles go through the natural stages of growth. Hair follicles naturally release strands and then begin to produce hair again in a cycle. Because this release is not simultaneous throughout the hair, we do not notice a change in density until an area of follicles stops entering the growth phase after shedding.

If palm-sized clumps of hair are coming out every time you detangle but you do not have a noticeable decrease in density at your scalp, it is probably breakage, not shedding. However, someone with super tight curls might see more hair in the shower on wash day because stray strands get trapped in the hair instead of falling. There are medical reasons for why someone may experience hair loss but we are not doctors. If you are experiencing a sudden increase in hair loss you should consult with your physician to rule out health-related causes.

HAIR-LOSS HABITS

Boredom or stress can lead to mindless tugging or twisting a section of hair. When this becomes a habit, it is hard to break, especially when it becomes subconscious. It is important to try and stop if you want to reduce your risk of hurting your hair follicles or causing breakage. Finding someone trustworthy who is often present in your life to give you a signal when you are fiddling with your hair can help you to break the habit.

Anything that causes tension at the scalp can cause premature hair loss and damage to the follicles, so be mindful of anything that pulls at your scalp. Your hair can get pulled throughout the night during a restless night of sleep as it rubs against your pillowcase. As mentioned previously, wearing a silk hair covering and/or using a silk pillowcase will help reduce friction. Frequent blow-drying and flat-ironing also pulls at the scalp and can cause increased hair loss.

Men's hair product commercials often show a man getting out of the shower and roughing up his hair with a towel. This is an obvious no-no because it causes frizz, but more importantly, it damages the hair follicles and leads to thinning hair over time. We recommend removing excess water by gently squeezing the hair with a towel.

It is important for your hair follicles to "breathe". Be mindful of how often you wear anything that prevents airflow at the scalp. Hats, scarves, and wigs are all great accessories, but make sure to take a break from them every so often.

CHAPTER 5: HAIRCUTS AND HAIR GROWTH

We need to eat, we need to drink water, and we need to sleep. However, we believe there is no such thing as *needing* a haircut. Cutting hair does not help it grow. As we mentioned earlier on, nothing that happens to hair beyond the scalp affects hair growth inside the follicle. So, when should you get haircuts? The answer is easy - when you want to.

Breakage and damage cause an unpleasant appearance and make hair less manageable and a haircut can help by removing that hair. However, it does not have to be removed. Not cutting it off is not going to damage the rest of your hair. However, continuing whatever behavior caused the original damage will cause more hair to become damaged, making the damage appear to be "spreading".

These are our suggestions to make your haircut look good for as long as possible:

- **Get a great haircut with a strong shape.** Uneven haircuts become more uneven as they grow. That is especially true for curly hair that loosens as it gets longer. The side or area that is longer will become more uneven as it grows and loosens. Haircuts on extra curly hair hold shape longer than haircuts on looser curl patterns because the hair grows in a tight circle and does not loosen much as it gets longer.
- **Avoid breakage.** Breakage does not happen evenly throughout the hair and will eventually cause an imbalanced haircut.
- **Don't do anything to change the visible wave or curl pattern.** Heat and chemical damage are the most common causes of

a change in curl pattern. If something loosens part of your hair it will immediately make the haircut lose its shape. For example, if the top layer of the hair becomes damaged more than the rest, that layer will become much more elongated and could put a lot of weight in the bottom of the hair, turning a rounded shape into a triangular shape. There is nothing wrong with triangular haircuts unless it is not what you want. There are no bad shapes or colors for that matter, only those you didn't desire but still received.

CURLY HAIRCUT TIPS
FOR STYLISTS

- **Don't rush your consultation.** You can be the best hairdresser on earth and still end up with an unhappy client if you do not ask detailed questions to really understand what your client wants. When they show photos, always ask what it is they like about the photo. Find out what their goals are for their hair in the future so that you can consider that when suggesting a haircut for them as well. Make sure that if you are giving them a style that requires more maintenance, they know that in advance.

- **Don't set your client up for disappointment.** Nowadays it is rare that a client will come in without some inspiration photos for their haircut. There is no possible way for their hair to look exactly like a photo of another person if it is going to be cut and worn in its natural state. There is no "same" when it comes to being natural. Try to help them understand how their look will differ.

- **Don't let curly bangs be an after-thought.** You need to know if your client wants a dramatic change like bangs before you start your service. Shrinkage is no joke for some curly hair types. A client with curls always needs to have their bangs cut dry at a longer position than they want them to be and then washed and styled and trimmed further if needed. The release of weight could also mean their hair will bounce up more in the days following the appointment. For hair types that are prone to shrinking, we recommend leaving the bangs a little longer than the desired length.

- **Don't razor-cut, slide-cut or use thinning shears.** Razor-cutting, thinning shears and slide-cutting hair will break up curl and wave formations by cutting through the wave or curl, making it become thinner and thinner as you move down the length of the hair. If you remove enough hairs from a natural wave or curl formation, then it may not curl at all. This also risks damaging the cuticle of the hair strand by slicing the hair vertically. This will increase tangling and porosity.

- **Don't assume how your client wants to be styled.** Not every curly wants control and not every wavy wants volume. Have a styling consultation with your client after they have been cut. Ask them what their "ideal result" would look like and let them know when there has to be a compromise. Most people want big, defined curls/waves AND big hair - but most people do not have the combination of density and hair type that allows for both. Remind them that pictures can be deceiving, so if they are seeing people with similar hair to them and a result you know only looks like that for a photo, let them know it! We are humans not magicians and it is always best to manage expectations so both of you can be happy with the result.

This last one is not a "don't", but rather a suggestion...

- **Teach your clients how to make their hair look just as good when they do it as when you do.** One of the greatest things about taking wavy and curly clients is that they don't want haircuts as often, which means even if you have a pretty full book of clients, you can still do something new. You want their haircut to look good for the months between their appointments (they are your walking billboards) so teach them how to style it themselves! Talk to them about what you are doing and why you are doing it while you style them. Make sure they understand the products you used, especially if they played a big role in the result. A happy, self-sufficient client may not come back often but trust us, you will be hearing from all of their family, friends and coworkers who will be eager to get in your chair once they see how great your client looks and hear what an awesome experience they had.

EXPECTATIONS AND PREPARATION FOR YOUR HAIRCUT

Going from healthy hair to damaged hair can affect the appearance of a haircut but so can the reverse situation. If your hair is currently unhealthy, an increase in hair health after a haircut can dramatically change the appearance of the haircut, especially if it is curly. When hair strands cannot properly bond together to form waves or curls, they cannot bounce up the way they will when healthy. For example, if layers or length are cut while they are unhealthy, they will bounce up and look significantly shorter when they become healthy. If you are unsure whether your hair is suitable to be cut, you should schedule a consultation with your stylist to determine if a change in product regimen should be followed for a certain amount of time prior to the appointment.

If you are going to cut a lot of the length off, it could take a few weeks or even longer for your strands to revert to their natural shape. If your hair is very long and you have fine, loose curls that mostly curl on the ends, cutting your hair shorter can make it seem like you cut your curls off but that is not the case. Healthy hair has memory. The bonds in the parts of the hair being pulled straight by length or from wearing it up often will stretch over time, making the natural wave or curl appear looser. The best thing you can do to get your strands back to normal is to minimize tension and weight as much as possible. If your hair looks less curly after a major haircut, give it a few weeks before making yourself (or your stylist) panic.

If you are considering a curly haircut, we are sure that you have spent some time looking at photos online for "inspiration". Keep in mind that everyone has a unique combination of texture and density, so no two curly-cuts can be the same. If you have

found a stylist whose work yo
suggest asking them to tell you wha.
think would work best for your hair and
face while letting them know your preferences such as length. Also mention any
haircut details you definitely want or do
not want like bangs and face-framing.

FINDING A WAVY OR CURLY HAIR SPECIALIST

Using location-specific hashtags is a great way to search for a curl specialist on social media. For example, we have clients who found us by searching "#orlandocurlyhair". Stylists with a professional Instagram account typically use it as a portfolio to show their work. When analyzing if a curl specialist is right for you, focus on the quality of their work and client testimonials, not their hair type or race. It is hard to break away from the feeling that we need to get our hair done by someone who looks like us, but doing so will expand your options and you could be missing out on the best haircut of your life by having tunnel vision.

Cutting curls is a skill that can be learned by any professional stylist. Having curly hair is not the reason we are good at working with curls. It does increase the bond with our clients because we have shared experiences when it comes to our hair, but you don't need to have curls to know how to properly cut them and understand the emotional history that comes along with curly clients. Compassion is key.

Stylists that specialize in cutting curly hair are currently a rare and unique breed. We invest in additional training that goes far beyond and outside of what we learned in cosmetology school. We keep our minds open to doing things in the way that works instead of following strict cutting rules.

A curly haircut needs to look good as a whole. It is not best performed by paying the most attention to the scalp and our fingers, but rather by paying attention to the person, the silhouette of the cut, and seeing how each snip changes the shape. Just like curl patterns are not uniform throughout the hair, neither is density, so we can't rely on technical uniformity when cutting. A curl specialist has to develop their eye in addition to their technique in order to shape the hair based on the client's unique curl patterns and differences in density. If you are having your hair cut in its natural state, it should be because you mostly wear it that way. It will look different when you manipulate it by straightening it, twisting it out, or anything else that stretches or shrinks your hair. Keep that in mind when choosing what kind of haircut to get.

Creating a beautiful silhouette on curly hair is an art and curly hair artists are in high demand. Most run their schedules by appointment only and are often booked out weeks or months in advance. Make sure to cancel and reschedule your appointments as soon as your plans change. If you expect your stylist to be there when you show up for your appointment, you should treat them with the same respect. With modern technology, there is really no excuse not to notify your stylist that you won't be able to make it to your appointment. Your appointment is important to you and important to your stylist, but it is just as important to someone who would love to be there in your place and can be if you cancel or reschedule at least a day before your appointment.

Diversity in the Salon - Keya Neal, Founder, @texturevsrace

"Separating race from the fabric of hair is a notion that has to be accepted by the salon and the client. Safe space salons are being created where you can feel comfortable and confident going into any salon. Researching your curl specialist, considering their body of work, and taking advantage of the opportunity to do a consultation will increase the likelihood of finding the right fit for you. Hair is not a race - it is a texture. Curl is the new race."

TIPS FOR GROWING OUT HAIR

Hair grows on average about half an inch per month. If you want to see that half inch increase in length it is of utmost importance to take care of your hair. Unhealthy hair will break off as fast as it grows, sometimes even faster, making it seem as though it stops growing at a certain length. That is not the case. As the amount of time since hair has left the follicle increases, the amount of weathering on the hair strand due to environmental and behavioral damage increases and so does the risk of breakage. As we already mentioned, cutting your ends off is not the strategy we recommend if your goal is long hair. The best way to get an increase in visible length as quickly as possible is to keep your ends so healthy that they don't break off or look so bad that you want to cut them off.

We have not seen evidence that scalp massage is scientifically proven to speed up hair growth, but if performed gently, you can at least enjoy the relaxation without damaging your hair. We recommend not using any tool but your fingers if you are going to do scalp massage. Breakage can occur very close to the scalp if tools or devices that create friction are used. If you can successfully minimize breakage and damage to your hair, you will see the same increase in length as the growth you see at your scalp. Your hair will seem to grow faster and will also be fuller than ever.

DIET AND HAIR HEALTH

As we mentioned earlier in the book, internal changes to your body will only impact new hair being formed inside the follicle. Proper nutrition won't fix damaged hair, but it will help new, healthy hair replace it at a faster pace. We know a healthy diet is necessary to support hair growth and a malnourished body can lead to weak hair and hair loss. However, we are not familiar with how nutrition can actually impact hair growth and health, so we decided to call upon our curl-friend Kelly Wilson, a certified Nutrition Coach, to ask for her input.

Kelly informed us that protein is a very important part of having healthy hair. She specifically recommended collagen protein for those who have a diet that includes animal products. As a vegan alternative, sea moss is an option due to its high mineral content, but its protein content is minimal. Both provide amazing benefits for hair, skin, and nails. She also noted the importance of protein in how the body processes B-vitamins. B-vitamins are important to the health of our bodies, including hair production. Supplements should not be necessary with a well-rounded diet, as B-vitamins are found in a wide array of meats, fish, vegetables, grains, and nuts. However, not consuming enough protein can inhibit the body's ability to absorb these vitamins.

The Dietary Reference Intake (DRI) is 0.36g of protein per pound of body weight for sedentary adults. How much additional protein you should consume depends on your activity level, age, and weight. Your recommended intake will be higher if you are active, pregnant, or lactating. To make it easy for you, the United States Department of Agriculture has a handy protein-intake calculator on its website: https://fnic.nal.usda.gov/fnic/dri-calculator/ .

CHAPTER 6: HAIR CHANGES DURING LIFE STAGES

Just like changes within our bodies are inevitable as we move through life, so are changes to our hair. Although we have little control over natural changes to our hair and bodies, it is beneficial to understand what is going on and why. It also helps to know how the new hair may be different, so we know how to treat it differently.

No matter how your body or your hair is changing as you go through the phases of life, do not become discouraged or feel bad. These are natural changes and so many people are going through the same thing at the same time. Remember that bearing a child is a blessing not everyone can have and that not everyone lives to see the natural phases that occur later in our lives. Changes can be a challenge but understanding what to expect and knowing you are not alone can help ease the process.

WISDOM GLITTER

Silver hair (or as we like to call it "wisdom glitter") comes at different times of life and in different amounts and areas for all people. We don't get to control where or when our glitter will arise but we can control how it looks and feels by understanding how it is different. We will tell you one thing you may have been wondering - plucking out your greys will not make them come back with a vengeance. However, plucking anywhere on your body causes trauma to the follicle and you could cause the follicle to stop producing new hair sooner than it would have otherwise.

Silver strands are not the same for everyone. Some people start getting grey and silver hairs that behave no differently than the rest of their hair. In that case, you would not have to treat them differently. Sometimes silver strands will be a different texture. They could be more fine or more coarse than the hair previously was. If your hair becomes more fine, you may need to use less styling product than before, since fine hair has a lower capacity for product. Vice versa, if your hair becomes more coarse, you may need to use more than before in order to get the result you desire.

You may notice a change in porosity between your old hair color and your wisdom glitter. If your silver strands seem dry, do not assume they are low porosity. Remember that low porosity hair repels water. If you're able to dunk your head underwater and your hair is heavier with water weight when you emerge, it is more likely to be high than low porosity. When hair becomes more porous it can lose moisture more easily and when it becomes less porous it is more difficult to get moisture inside to begin with. If your porosity changes, follow our guide from earlier in the book for determining your porosity and our suggestions to work with it.

If your silver hairs take on a yellow tint,

using a purple shampoo can help. The purpose of purple shampoo is to tone out yellow because purple and yellow are across from each other on the color wheel. The shampoo needs to get deep into the hair strand to change the visible color of the hair. Pollutants like smoke are often the cause of yellowing and they can become locked inside the cortex. A harsh cleanser will do a better job pulling the yellow out of the hair while simultaneously neutralizing the yellow with a purple additive but it can cause dryness. A sulfate-free, high-quality purple shampoo will be more gentle and safer for frequent use.

You may decide to cover your silvers with hair dye. In most cases, silver hairs are harder to penetrate. That is why colorists typically need to use stronger developers, dyes with extra pigment, and/or increased processing times when trying to color silver hair. Stronger developer helps to open the cuticle and keep it open long enough for the change in pigment to occur. Box-dyes have very strong developers that are able to cover silver but the damage may not be worth it. If you think managing silver hair is difficult, trust us, managing damaged hair is worse.

If you have been coloring your hair you may decide you want to stop and embrace your silver strands. The transition can be tricky, especially if your previous color was dark. It may be tempting to try and lighten all of your color-processed hair to bring it closer to the silver color. Removing previous color can be damaging, expensive, and time-consuming. There are other options. Switching from permanent color to a grey-blending color can help ease the transition without having to damage your color-processed hair. These are hair dyes specifically formulated to be more translucent. You will see a little bit of the silver hairs but not as much contrast as there would be if you discontinue coloring completely. If you eventually stop doing color completely, the contrast between the silver hairs and the grey-blending color will be less as well.

The transition away from color-processing can be easier if you were doing highlights previously. Blonde is a much closer shade to silver and grey than darker hair colors. Highlighting techniques can be used to blend greys. Letting some silvers show between highlights can help your new strands come in less abruptly. Adding highlights to previously colored hair will also decrease the contrast.

If you're going to stop dyeing or highlighting and let the silvers take over, wide headbands and scarves are accessory options that can help make the transition easier without spending any time or money in the salon. You can style your hair to conceal your roots until they are long enough that you're willing to cut the rest off for a full wisdom-glitter takeover.

Whether you decide to cover or embrace your hair as it changes is up to you. Some people lean into their new strands right away and some may color their hair for the rest of their life. As with any other decision made about your hair, there is no right or wrong. Do what makes *you* feel good.

HORMONE CHANGES

During pregnancy, hair growth tends to pick up speed. It is also common to notice an increase in retention of hair (less shedding), making the hair become more dense. Unfortunately, after giving birth, many women will experience significant shedding. Sometimes they will shed hair to a lower density than they had pre-pregnancy. This can happen because of the dramatic hormone changes that occur after giving birth, especially if vitamins and supplements that were impacting hormones are discontinued. The hair usually fills back in with time.

Menopause also causes a change in hormones that can impact hair. Loss of density (increased shedding) and new hair growing in with a finer texture is common. Hot flashes can cause the scalp to sweat profusely, causing hair to stick to the scalp and natural oils to build up faster. More frequent cleansing may be needed after a woman enters menopause.

"CHEMO-CURLS"

Hair loss during chemotherapy treatment and then new growth being curly, even if it was not before, is a common occurrence among patients who choose chemotherapy treatment. Given the nickname "chemo-curls", hair that grows in curly after treatment is discontinued is often very fine texture, almost like baby hairs. This means it can easily be weighed down by conditioner and styling products.

Even if you had curls before treatment, the texture and porosity may be different now, so you may want to shift your styling routine and products. There is no definite evidence as to why the hair comes in curly, but because the shape of the follicle impacts the curl pattern and the size impacts the texture, it makes sense to us that chemotherapy drugs may impact the shape and size of the follicles. Whether this change is permanent is unknown to us, but we hope this book will help you navigate your new texture as best as possible, no matter how long it sticks around.

Medical conditions and treatments that cause hair loss are only one of the many reasons we want to normalize wig-wearing. It is hard enough to be so sick but to also feel like you will stand out or be treated differently for not having hair or for wearing a wig is unnecessary salt in the wound. There is no reason we should feel less comfortable in a wig than we do in our own hair. We do not need hair to be healthy and we should not need it to be happy. If more healthy people with hair of their own would shave their heads and/or wear wigs "just because," it would help eliminate the social stigma surrounding wig-wearing and baldness.

LIL' CURLIES

As far as products go, infants do not need special products for their hair. Shampoos marketed for babies often claim to be "tear-free" but that does not always mean harsh-chemical-free. The same information on navigating ingredients that we provide later in this book can be used to choose products for children as well. The biggest difference between the hair and scalp of infants and adults is that babies' and infants' scalps produce less sebum. This means that they do not need their hair washed as often as adults do.

Babies and toddlers typically have very fine hair which can become more coarse as they grow up. As they get older, their hair will change so their needs will change. Don't be afraid though! You can handle it. With this book as a resource, you will have everything you need to make adjustments as they grow and eventually pass it on to them to begin caring for their own hair.

Confidence will give kids power but their self-esteem is under attack by social media. It is extremely important that we make sure they think just as highly of their hair as we do. The standards of beauty have never been harder to keep up with because of how quickly they can change now.

Hair in its natural state is completely unique to each individual. That means we have to be comfortable with ourselves in order to really love our hair as it naturally is. There is no way to be "the same" unless our hair is manipulated out of its natural state. It is cool to be different but being different can be especially difficult for children and teens. We can help them see the ways they are unique as their best traits by teaching them words of affirmation.

THE DREADED "PICTURE DAY" - DENNIS' HAIR STORY

Although I don't recall being bullied for my curly hair growing up, I definitely had certain experiences where I felt isolated because of my curls. Growing up in Guayaquil, Ecuador, I don't remember knowing any other kids who had curly hair. I remember every year at school they would have a professional photographer come in to take our portraits. Every single photo day was the same - I would do my best to look nice - and then out would come the fine-tooth comb. The photographer would rip it through my hair trying to "smooth" it down and it would do exactly the opposite.

It is too bad they could not let me decide how my hair would be for the photo or listen to me when I said the comb would not help. It is hard as a kid to feel like you do not have control over so many things. I liked my curls but not after they were combed through. I preferred the photos my parents would take but unfortunately you don't get to submit your own school portraits. I am glad that there is more awareness now of what to do and not to do to curly hair. Hopefully there are less children having bad picture-days just because someone else doesn't understand their hair.

CHAPTER 7: NAVIGATING PRODUCT TYPES

In recent years, there has been a major boom in the marketing of products specifically for waves, curls and coils. Between professional brands, drugstore brands, and the seemingly hundreds of indie brands that pop up on our social media feeds, it can be overwhelming (to say the least) when we try to decide what products to use.

We will not be discussing specific brands for the purpose of this book. One of the main purposes of this book is for you to be able to choose the right products for you without having to focus on brand names. This way no matter where you live, where you go, or what your budget is, you can find something that works for you.

HAIR CLEANSERS

We believe you should wash your hair. Most sebum, hair product, and dirt cannot be broken down by water alone. We also believe shampoos that lather are not harmful to all hair types. Some people require a stronger cleanse to remove excess sebum buildup if they have an oily scalp. Selecting the right type of cleanser for your hair and scalp is key to keeping your hair in balance so that you do not experience buildup or dryness.

Cleansers that lather are called shampoos. The ingredients in your shampoo are more important than whether it lathers, but the ingredients that cause the lather tend to also remove significant dirt, oil and product from the hair and scalp. That is why there is a fear of lather among people who have dry hair. However, not all lather cleansers cause dryness. We will talk more about the cleansing ingredients used in all kinds of cleansers in the next chapter so that you can look at bottles of shampoo and determine which will be stronger and which will be more gentle. Some shampoos will advertise their strength if they are marketing the product to someone who needs a very deep cleanse.

Clarifying and chelating shampoos are intended to be the strongest of all lathering cleansers. They are designed to rid the hair and scalp of impurities. However, they are not the same. Clarifying shampoos are meant to break down build up from hair products and excess sebum. Chelating shampoos are stronger and designed specifically for the purpose of removing mineral buildup that comes from hard water.

Ideally, you find a cleanser that keeps your hair and scalp in balance so that clarifying is not needed. If you live somewhere with hard water, occasionally using a chelating shampoo may be something you want in your regimen. Water filters are available that can help soften the water. How often you shampoo depends on your lifestyle and personal preference. We say wash your hair when it feels dirty but if it is feeling dirty often, it may be time to revisit the ingredients you are using in your cleanser, conditioner and styling products. You may be using products that are either rapidly causing buildup or not breaking down products with a strong enough cleanse. We will go into ingredients in detail later on in the book.

No-lather cleansers, which differ from the co-washes we will discuss next, will gently cleanse the hair and scalp. They work great for someone who has dry or damaged hair but does not want the weight of a co-wash. However, if your scalp is prone to sebum buildup, you may want to alternate with a lather shampoo especially if you are active. If you use styling products that cannot be rinsed off with just water, they could also build up without a lather shampoo.

Another popular choice of cleanser is called a "co-wash". There is a lot of confusion surrounding co-washes. What does co-wash mean? Co-wash is the abbreviation and hyphenation of "conditioner" and "wash". The term "co-wash" was first used to describe rinsing and conditioning your hair but skipping shampoo entirely. You would say, "I am co-washing my hair today" to describe the act of only rinsing and conditioning. However, conditioner does not have cleansing agents in it. When it does, it falls into the cleanser category.

Cleansing agents have been added to conditioners to create "co-washes". The word has become a noun through social media and marketing efforts. Co-washes are sold as cleansers that do not lather and have the look, feel, and weight of conditioners. Now we can also say, "I am using a co-wash today". The difference between using a co-wash and "washing with conditioner" is that conditioners do not contain cleansing agents and co-washes do. They typically contain gentle cleansing agents and heavy ingredients so they double as gentle cleanser and conditioner.

Co-washes add weight to hair the way that

conditioner does and remove little sebum and product buildup. No-lather cleansers will gently remove a small amount of sebum and product buildup without adding weight. Shampoo that lathers will leave your hair and scalp with the lightest, cleanest feeling. There are stronger shampoos, such as clarifying and chelating, for those who experience buildup beyond the normal level that is caused by sebum or products between shampoos. Which is best for you depends on the needs of your hair and scalp.

How often you cleanse depends on your lifestyle and personal preferences. The most important thing is that you should not be afraid to wash your hair. With high-quality ingredients that keep your hair in balance, you can wash your hair whenever you become uncomfortable with how it feels or if you want to start over with your style.

Using a shampoo every wash might work great for one person but alternating between a shampoo and a co-wash works better for someone else. Different people will have different hair, different scalps, and different lifestyles and so they have different cleansing needs. There is nothing wrong with being different; but it is wrong not to respect each others' differences.

CONDITIONERS, DEEP CONDITIONERS, AND MASKS

Most conditioners add weight to the hair and leave it feeling soft. Believe it or not, conditioner is not a necessity for everyone. Cream-based products deposit weight into the hair strand. More weight is not beneficial to all hair types. People with fine hair and those who like volume will experience unpleasant weight from conditioner. If you have a healthy, functioning cuticle, conditioner is not needed. The cuticle will lock in moisture and make your hair soft and shiny without need for conditioner. Try it if you haven't already done so. Nothing bad will happen if you do not like the result but something amazing could happen if you do!

A conditioner is not a deep-conditioner just because the label says so. "Deep" is an adverb, so calling a conditioner deep is describing something that it does. Companies have created products specifically called "deep-conditioners" to convince us to buy more products, instead of deep conditioning with the conditioner that we already have. Penetrating the hair strand deeply can be achieved with any conditioner and so any conditioner can be a deep conditioner. Deep-conditioning involves keeping the cuticle open while the hair is wet for an extended amount of time (usually a minimum of 5 minutes) to allow the product to penetrate the hair strand deeper than it would otherwise.

"Masks" tend to have a much thicker consistency than other conditioners. In addition to penetrating the hair strand when the cuticle opens up, they coat the hair, making it easier to ensure that the cuticle is also benefiting from the conditioner. If you can't decide on a conditioner or a mask, you may want to consider ingredients instead. It is what your conditioner or mask is made of that is the most important as to whether it will benefit your hair or not. We will discuss ingredients in the next chapter.

STYLING PRODUCTS

"If you look like this - buy this" is an easy way to market products. However, it does not always lead to the best purchase decisions because brands make assumptions about different hair types. For example: a product that is marketed as being for extra curly hair is most likely going to have a lot of heavy ingredients; products for wavy hair will be lighter. We should not assume that all tighter curl patterns desire weight and all looser patterns desire volume. Styling products should be chosen based on what you want. This means ignoring any mention of curl pattern on a product and just reading what it says it *does*.

We recommend using new stylers alone the first time you use them so that you understand what purpose they serve. If you combine multiple products without understanding what they each do for you, it is like walking into your closet with no idea whether you should be putting on a sweater or a tank top. You could walk out wearing two sweaters and no pants if you don't understand what purpose each item in the closet serves. When you do understand what each one does, then you can create combinations suited to the look you are trying to achieve or find an amazing all-in-one product that provides your desired result on its own.

Your styling products are your wardrobe, but it is what lies underneath them that is most important. Styling products will not deliver the results they promise if the hair underneath is unhealthy. Styling products are not solutions but they can cause problems on their own. Styling products that are applied to wet hair and then left in the hair for days can have a negative impact if the ingredients are harmful. Choosing ingredients that are not right for your climate can also disrupt your style. Understanding ingredients is the most important part of choosing products. Let's get to it.

CHAPTER 8: NAVIGATING INGREDIENT TYPES

In short: the only *bad* ingredients are those which are unsafe for cosmetic use. It is time to decriminalize ingredients that are simply misunderstood. We are going to help you understand the purpose and value of different kinds of ingredients but this will not be an all-inclusive list of everything you may find in your products. We will, however, provide you with the resources to dig deeper into specific ingredients if you desire.

There are a lot of long and confusing ingredient names and the popular ingredients used in cosmetics are changing all the time. That is why checking labels regularly is important. Unfortunately, cosmetics are not required to go under any safety testing by the U.S. Food and Drug Administration, also known as the FDA, before they are brought to market. Knowing this, it is even more important that we learn the purpose and effect of ingredients and how to navigate ingredient lists on products to the best of our ability.

Most brands will list the ingredients in their products in order of predominance. This means that the first ingredient on the list is the ingredient that makes up the highest percentage of the total composition. The first ingredient is usually water. The second ingredient makes up the second-largest percentage, and so on. We suggest focusing your attention on the first five ingredients on a label because these will most likely have the greatest impact on your hair.

You can go to the Environmental Working Group's website for more information on specific cosmetic ingredients, their uses, and their safety ratings. The US National Library of Medicine's PubChem website is another great resource for finding scientific information about specific ingredients and other chemicals.

Some ingredients work well for some people and not for others. If you are having a negative reaction to something, stop using it. Otherwise, if you find something that works, do not concern yourself with whether other people think it is good or bad. They may have had a personally bad experience but that doesn't mean you will.

Our goal with this book is to inform you so that you can make educated decisions when it comes to products for your own hair or the hair of someone you are caring for. The information provided in the sections of this chapter will help you understand ingredients, what they do and who they are best for so that you can determine what to look for and what to avoid in your products.

SURFACTANTS

The word "surfactant" comes from the three words: "surface active agent". They are used in cleansers to create a lather and remove dirt and buildup from the surface of the hair and scalp. For a long time, sulfates were the primary surfactant in most shampoos. As consumer knowledge of ingredients increased, the word sulfate was put on the ingredient blacklist and suddenly it seems like every product no matter the quality or price is sulfate-free.

We suggest you avoid sulfates *only if* you have hair or a scalp that is prone to dryness. If you are prone to sebum and product buildup, washing with a sulfate shampoo might be the "fresh start" your hair and scalp needs. However, over-washing can cause a dry scalp and the sebaceous glands may start working hard to replenish the dry scalp. This will lead to even worse sebum buildup and the desire to wash even more frequently. Limiting sulfate shampoo to once a week is what we suggest.

There are *lots* of other surfactants found in hair cleansers. We are not going to list every single ingredient in existence but we will cover the categories of surfactants which will help you navigate which types to look for in your cleanser. There are synthetic surfactants, naturally-derived (but synthetically-processed) surfactants and completely natural surfactants. Which you should look for in your cleanser depends on how gentle a cleanser your hair and scalp need.

Both synthetic and naturally-derived surfactants can be processed at different quality levels so we cannot say that everything synthetic is bad and everything naturally-derived is good. Two ingredients can be listed by the same exact name but differ in quality due to how they were processed. However, if we are talking about two surfactants in products at a similar price point, the naturally-derived surfactant should provide a more gentle cleanse than the purely synthetic surfactant. Completely natural surfactants do exist but for most people they will not be cleansing enough for long-term use and they are not found in most commercial hair products because they usually expire quickly.

Your surfactants in your cleansers will always be toward the beginning of the list of ingredients. You can spot a naturally-derived surfactant on an ingredient list because they usually involve the word "coco" or "coca" somewhere in the name. For example, "sodium cocoyl isethionate" is a common naturally-derived surfactant. Synthetic surfactants often have the word "laureth" or "lauroyl" somewhere in the name. For example, "sodium lauroyl isethionate" is a common synthetic surfactant. You can do research online to find out whether the surfactants in a cleanser are naturally-derived or completely synthetic.

HUMECTANTS AND ANTI-HUMECTANTS

The purpose of humectants in hair products is to attract water into the hair. Glycerin and propylene glycol are two of the most popular humectants found in hair products. The most important thing to understand about humectants is how they function in different climates.

Humidity refers to the amount of moisture in the air. The higher the humidity - the more moisture there is in the air. A humidity percentage between 40 and 50%, known as moderate, is commonly considered the most comfortable. Below 40% is considered dry and above 50% is considered humid.

Humectants perform best in moderate climates. When the air is dry, humectants can pull moisture out of the hair. When the air is humid, humectants can pull too much moisture into the hair, causing the cortex to swell and push open the cuticle and it is likely that definition will be lost.

Lower porosity types will benefit the most and face the least risk of losing their style from humectants. The cuticle of higher porosity types will not be in a low enough position to stop the transfer of moisture into or out of the hair in a dry or humid climate.

Putting a layer of an anti-humectant on top of styling products that contain humectants can help prevent the transfer of moisture. Any substance that repels water functions as an anti-humectant.

SILICONE AND "POLYQUATS"

Silicones are great for creating shine, locking in moisture and blocking out humidity. "Polyquats" (scientifically known as polymers designated as a polyquaternium) can help smooth a damaged cuticle, reduce flyaway hair and static, aid in detangling, and provide conditioning benefits. Most silicone ingredients are easy to identify because they often end in "-cone". You can identify polyquats on an ingredient list because they will usually be listed as "Polyquaternium-" followed by a number between 1 and 37.

Not all silicones and polyquats are created equal because some dissolve in water and others do not. Ingredients that are not water-soluble can build up on hair and create unpleasant weight, but that does not mean they have to be avoided. Your cleanser just needs to be powerful enough to remove your styling products. If you need to use a very gentle cleanser because your hair is prone to dryness, then we suggest sticking with water-soluble ingredients in your hair products.

You can test if a product is water-soluble by applying it to your skin and trying to rinse it off with only water. Warm water will break down buildup much better than cooler water. If it does not come off with just water, try washing it off with your hair cleanser. Even if a product is not water-soluble, as long as your cleanser removes the product, it should not cause build up on your hair.

OILS AND BUTTERS

Raw oils and butters are not moisturizers. For something to moisturize the hair, it needs to hydrate and hydration occurs with water. When absorbed, they can soften the hair, but they are not a replacement for water. Some raw oils and butters can build up because they are hard to remove even with cleansers. This can cause increased dryness as water is blocked from entering the hair strand over time.

If the molecules of the oil or butter do not absorb into the hair strand, they act as a sealant because they will stop the transfer of water into or out of the hair. If they do absorb then they can soften the hair, but the cuticle openings need to be larger than the molecules of the substance in order to absorb. Molecule sizes can differ depending on how the oil or butter was processed.

It is hard to predict if molecules will pass

through cuticle openings so, if you like the effect of oils or butters, we suggest using hair products that contain hydrolyzed amounts. Molecules become much smaller when ingredients are hydrolyzed. They are designed to penetrate the hair strand along with the rest of the ingredients in the product.

ALCOHOL

"Short-chain alcohols" are typically only found in styling products and they reduce moisture and drying time. Products with these alcohol types can dehydrate strands, forming a strong hold and a stiff cast. However, that is not necessarily bad for everyone. Decreasing water-content in the hair will cause styling products to have a stronger hold and some people will sacrifice softness for control. In this case, styling products with short-chain alcohols might give a desirable result.

Hair that is prone to dryness should avoid styling products that contain short-chain alcohols as they could cause extreme dryness and breakage with continued use. Some common short-chain alcohols in hair products are "alcohol denat" and "SD alcohol".

Not all types of alcohol dry out hair. Some

alcohol types actually act as conditioning agents. These are called "fatty alcohols". The ones that are most common in hair products are cetyl alcohol and cetearyl alcohol.

There are two more types of alcohols that do not fit into either of these categories: "propylene glycol" and "benzyl alcohol". Propylene glycol can attract water into hair and so it is sometimes used as a humectant. Benzyl alcohol is found in hair products as a preservative. It can negatively impact dry hair and has a reputation for causing an allergic reaction for those with very sensitive skin.

PRESERVATIVES

Preservatives are used in hair products to increase the item's ability to survive storage and distribution and sit on the shelf of a store for as long as possible without expiring, also known as shelf-life. They also keep bacteria from growing once they are exposed to air and contact with microorganisms.

Fewer preservatives means a lower shelf-life and a lower shelf-life means that the company needs to increase the price of the product in order to make a profit. That is why we see the cheapest products in huge drugstores. Inexpensive preservatives can negatively impact hair, especially if it is already prone to dryness.

Parabens are a type of preservative with much controversy surrounding their use in cosmetics. There is speculation circulating regarding the safety of parabens, but no research has been conclusive that they are definitely dangerous to human health. We believe that speculation of safety is reason enough to avoid parabens, especially when there are so many other kinds of preservatives at the disposal of cosmetic companies.

PROTEIN (& MOISTURE)

It is a common misconception created by the social media grapevine that protein and moisture behave like a seesaw: when one goes up, the other goes down, and vice versa. It is true that protein and moisture should be in "balance". However, that balance means each being at their individual normal, healthy levels. In fact, damaged hair can benefit from both because protein bonds are weakened and moisture is lost when hair is damaged.

Our hair is made of keratin protein. Healthy hair has all the protein it needs and doing protein treatments on healthy hair can make it dry and brittle. Adding moisture is not the solution to using too much protein - discontinuing protein treatments is. Although conditioner after a protein treatment that causes dryness may make it feel better, it does not change the fact that protein was added to the hair that was not needed. Breakage can still occur with on-going use, no matter how much condition-ing is done before or after.

We do not recommend protein treatment unless you are sure that your hair is se-verely damaged. To maintain a healthy protein level, look for products that have hydrolyzed proteins in them. These micro-scopic amounts will act as over-the-coun-ter supplements to help keep normal pro-tein levels in check. Hydrolyzed protein amounts in shampoos, conditioners, and styling products are so small that they should not cause hair to become stiff and break.

HOW "SAFE" INGREDIENTS CAN BECOME UNSAFE - STEPHANIE'S (SECOND & UNEXPECTED) HAIR STORY

At the start of 2019, the products I was using on my hair to keep it healthy for years suddenly started to cause hair damage and hair loss from my scalp. (I won't name the company but if you do a little digging online you will figure it out for yourself.) My theory is that a change in ownership led to a change in storage facilities and that the warehouses where the products were being stored were no longer climate-controlled. I believe high levels of heat caused a harmless ingredient (I suspect a preservative) to release a harmful chemical into the bottles of product - potentially formaldehyde or something like it. Heat can cause a chemical reaction for many ingredients so it is important that cosmetics are always in a cool, dry place and especially away from high temperatures.

My hair health took a slow decline for a few months that I blamed on humidity. However, everything changed when I started going to high-heat workout classes with the styling products in my hair. They were exposed to over 100-degree heat for an hour a few times a week. My body had never been healthier, but within a few short months my hair was destroyed. That was when the extent of my damage became so extreme that I could no longer ignore it or blame it on the weather, "too much moisture", "too much protein", or having highlighted my hair not long before. This was beyond any color damage, or any other kind of damage, I had ever seen on myself or another person. It definitely was not an allergic reaction because hair can not have an allergic reaction to something. The cells of hair are dead.

In early September when I went to Orlando to take care of my clients, I realized that all of those who were using the same brand were having the same issues. I finally discovered the cause was the products, but it was too late for my hair. We currently do not know what ingredient caused the damage to occur, but we are working hard to find out and bring this issue to light.

By mid-September, after many attempts to save my hair with products and treatments, we realized it was beyond repair. It was breaking off faster than it was growing. I knew if I didn't rid myself of this hair, it was going to leave on its own anyway. Dennis gave me a cute edgy bob to get rid of a lot of the damage, but it became evident that the damage reached all the way to my scalp. I could have held onto the damaged hair, but my hair was so destroyed that I had to sweep the floor of my apartment daily to get rid of the long, warped strands of hair.

My hair only 3 months before I had to cut it from damage.

My hair the day that I cut it to start over again.

When October came, I only had a little less than an inch of healthy new growth but I was ready to cut it and put this whole experience behind me. It was so unmanageable and I was exhausted. I had to find the positive and move forward. I learned so much and was able to help so many people through this challenging experience. It opened my eyes in so many ways. I lost a lot of hair, but I gained way more value than hair could ever give me.

Dennis and I already had a trip planned for the first week of October so I could meet my new friend, Amber Pearson, also a wavy and curly specialist, in Salt Lake City. Before our trip, she told me that if I wanted to cut my hair she would do it with me - just as short if not shorter than I needed to go. She did not have to do so and I did not encourage her, but she insisted anyway. This was only one of the countless ways Amber has supported me on my journey since getting on YouTube. (Thank you, Amber. Our friendship is evidence that social media can actually breed really amazing connections if we use it to love instead of hate).

My hair is so short now that it will barely form a curl. I will be honest and tell you it's not always easy seeing Dennis' long curly locks (he stopped using the brand before we started going to the hot work-out classes). I have had plenty of moments where a pang of jealousy sets in, like when he nonchalantly pulls his hair into a bun or plays around with how he can style it. I start having thoughts like, "my hair would be so long and beautiful by now if....." and then I try to stop myself there. This is not productive thinking. There was noth-ing I could have done differently in the past without the knowledge I have now and there is nothing I can do to bring it back any faster than nature will permit.

I plan to grow my hair back out and use it as an opportunity to coach other people online who are also growing out a very short cut. It isn't easy, but I have done it before, and I can do it again and this time I will share my experience. I will do my best to enjoy the journey because life is too precious to spend looking in the mirror every day and wishing you looked different. The presence, quality, and length of our hair does not increase or decrease our value as a person.

Hair is not who we are any more than our nails or eye color are who we are. Hair is aesthetic. It is not an identity and for many it is a luxury. Remember that before you ever let another good day become a bad one because of your hair.

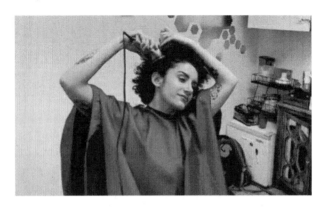

CHAPTER 9: NAVIGATING PRODUCT AND INGREDIENT QUALITY

A major myth that needs debunking is that our hair gets "used to" product over time. Whoever started that rumor on the social media grapevine must have been working for a low-quality hair product brand. By blaming our hair for the fact that their low-quality products have a negative impact over time, we are likely to keep buying product from that brand.

Bouncing around from one low-quality product to another based on this idea is like switching from a fast-food chain that sells burgers to a fast-food chain that sells tacos every few weeks thinking that we just got used to burgers. Tacos every other month might make us feel different, but it will not improve our health in the long run.

Unfortunately, we can not stop hair products from being marketed as good for our hair when they are not. Distinguishing between what is good for us and what is not involves understanding where we should get our hair products from and which products are best for our hair if we want them to have a better impact on our hair health and appearance.

PROFESSIONAL AND DRUGSTORE PRODUCTS

We believe the safest bet is to buy products at a reputable hair salon. Salons are typically selective about the quality of the products they use and sell to clients. Client-satisfaction is of utmost importance to business-savvy salon owners and that includes the results that clients and customers experience from home hair care products bought from the salon.

We believe the second-safest option is to visit retailers, in-store or online, that specialize in high-end beauty products. These stores typically offer quite a few brands that are also carried in salons. Because beauty products are their specialty, the warehouses they use should be climate-controlled to protect the quality of the products stored in them. Some of these retailers have both drugstore and professional sections. We recommend sticking to the professional offerings.

We recognize that high-quality products are not within reach for everyone. Although we do not recommend purchasing cosmetics at the drugstore, we will still share some information to help understand their products a little better. The surfactants in drugstore co-washes are typically not as harsh as those in drugstore shampoos. Look for naturally-derived surfactants which are typically more gentle than purely synthetic. If a co-wash is too heavy, shampoos that are labeled as daily shampoos tend to have more gentle cleansers.

Unfortunately, it is common to find brands in drug stores that do not have authorization from the company for their products to be sold there. This occurs because of something called diversion. Sometimes these products are counterfeit or contaminated. Diverted products may be real, but even so, they could be expired. There are currently no laws prohibiting drug stores from selling unauthorized products they purchased from third-party distributors.

Brands will only guarantee the quality of products sold by authorized retailers. You can usually find a list on their website. Red flags that a product was diverted include outdated packaging, a hidden expiration date, or a retail price that is different from the price shown on the brand's website.

CHAPTER 10: HOW TO SPEND LESS MONEY ON PRODUCTS

The reality is that we live in a society focused on treatment rather than prevention because treatment makes companies more money. Hair product brands want us to wait for buildup, dryness, or damage to arise, spend money buying more products attempting to fix it, and then repeat the behavior that caused it. It is a cycle that benefits the brand - not the consumer.

Some of the techniques for using curly hair

products also lead to way more spending and waste. Diluting our hair products with loads of water causes us to need to use more to get any kind of effect from the product. Applying it by squeezing also causes waste. All of these things combined lead to consumers burning through products which creates a constant flow of purchasing and the belief that investing in high-quality product is not feasible because so much product is used so quickly.

Just like with diet and exercise, lifelong positive results involve sticking to a good routine. As we mentioned earlier, it isn't true that you need to change products all the time in order to keep your hair healthy. That can become very expensive very fast and is even worse if you never end up finishing the products or make yourself use products you do not like just to finish them up. Find what works for you and stick with it to get the best results long-term and spend less money than you do when experimenting.

Once you have found the best products for

your hair, look online or check in-store to see which of your products are available in a larger size. Buying a larger size always decreases the cost per ounce of the product. A high-quality product can sometimes cost you the same (per ounce) as a drugstore product when purchased in a larger size bottle.

MASSAGING-IN >
"SQUISHING"-OUT

When you squeeze or squish product into your hair, it is also squeezed *out.* We have another suggestion that will help you use less product and is just as, if not more, effective at helping your products absorb.

We choose to massage conditioner and styling products into hair so that we can use less, waste less, and increase absorption of the product. Our reasoning is drawn from a comparison to absorption of products on skin. When you want something to absorb into your skin - you massage it. We find that the same thing works for hair.

This and other techniques discussed in this book have corresponding video clips on our YouTube channel. If you are viewing the e-book version, you can click on the technique title to go straight to the video. For paperback readers and audio-listeners, please visit *https://www.youtube.com/ StephanieandDennisMero* and find the playlist "CTCC Demos" . Did you know? If you purchased the paperback on Amazon, you can add the e-book for only $2.99 and download the free Kindle app for your phone so you can take us everywhere.

MULTI-PURPOSE YOUR SHAMPOO

Ever wondered why men are marketed "all in one" cleansers that give them the ability to have a maximum of one or two things in their shower, but women seem to need three or four products just to do one thing? It is not a difference in the hair and skin of men and women - it is marketing.

We started washing our faces and bodies with our gentle, lather shampoo a little under a year ago and our skin is now softer and smoother even though we are older and certainly getting less sleep. If you are using a "co-wash" or no-lather cleanser to wash your hair, you may have a harder time using it as your body and/or face wash. However, if you have a shampoo that works wonders for your hair and scalp, it may just work for your body too.

CHAPTER 11: INTRODUCTION TO STYLING

You made it! You learned about the science behind hair and scalp care, how to navigate products and ingredients, and now you get to put all that knowledge to use in creating your own styling methods.

We are going to share with you how to choose products for your style and our techniques for styling. These techniques can be used on all wave and curl patterns. If a technique will be best for certain porosity types, we will tell you. After you have completed our styling chapters, you will understand what different techniques achieve and how to combine them to create your own looks.

If uniformity is perfection, then there is nothing natural about perfection. Porosity and density vary throughout the hair of every human being. Both play a role in how strands will bond together to form the visible appearance of individual curl, wave and coil formations. Because of this, the sizes and shapes will not be uniform throughout your hair.

You can choose to spend more time and effort in an attempt for uniformity, but please do not put out into the world that you spent any less time or effort than you actually did to achieve that look. You will set unrealistic expectations for people who are trying to simplify their routine and be happy with it.

Be mindful of the goals you set for your styling result. If you use the result of someone else's styling method as a goal when you replicate that method on your own hair; there is no way you will succeed. We need to compare our styling results to only our own previous styling results or we will never be satisfied.

FRIZZ: TO FIGHT OR BEFRIEND?

Frizz, or flyaways, are individual strands that went astray from their curl or wave formation. This can happen for many reasons and is not always an indicator of hair that is dry or damaged. Unless you are never going to leave the house you will not be able to avoid frizz completely, but understanding the styling tips in this book will help you minimize it.

Higher porosity types are the most prone to frizz occuring after styling is complete. This happens because the cuticle does not do a great job at locking the style in place and blocking moisture from entering or leaving the hair strand. Products can either make this worse or help prevent it from happening.

As we discussed earlier, using humectants

in a dry or humid climate can also cause the cuticle to open or moisture to release. Styling products that create a strong seal will help keep your style together but striving for a head free of stray strands may be a fruitless endeavor. Frizz happens. If we do our best to accept or embrace it, we will be much happier. Remember that no one is paying as much attention to your frizz as *you* are. (But if you complain about it - you're pointing it out!)

WATER TEMPERATURE AND AIR TEMPERATURE

There is a lot of misinformation about how different temperatures of water and air impact hair during the washing and styling process. Here is our super-simple breakdown:

- **Warm Water**: Breaks down product and sebum buildup, increases fading of artificial hair-color, and raises the cuticle.
- **Cold Water**: Gently rinses hair with little buildup removal, prolongs hair-color life, and lowers (but does not seal) the cuticle.
- **Warm Air**: Speeds up drying time by helping water evaporate. Warm air applied to completely dry hair will slightly raise the cuticle, allowing minor adjustments in the hairstyle, set in place when cooled down.
- **Cold Air**: Helps seal the cuticle and lock the shape of the hair strands in posi-

tion. Gravity may impact the amount a curl or wave loosens, but the strands will do their best to stay in the position where they went from warm and dry to cool and dry. This is called "setting" the style.

CHAPTER 12: STYLING PRODUCT SELECTION

Brands should not assume that everyone with wavy hair wants volume and everyone with curly hair wants control. We suggest you ignore any mention of hair type (e.g., wavy or curly) when you read the label of a styling product. Focus on the words that describe what the product does rather than who it says it is for.

For example, if a product says it "elongates" but it also says "extra curly hair" it leads you to believe that someone who doesn't have that hair type could not use it to elongate their hair. That is not true. It will also elongate the hair of someone with loose curls or waves and they can use that same styling product if that is what they wish to achieve.

PRODUCTS FOR DEFINITION AND CONTROL

We consider conditioner a styling product. Conditioner adds weight to your hair, even if you do not leave it in your hair as a styler. How much weight your conditioner will add depends on how you rinse it. If you rinse with cool or cold water, you will not rinse out as much conditioner as if you rinse warm, and you will add more weight to the result of your style.

Leave-in conditioners and cream-based styling products create definition from the inside-out. As long as they fully absorb, they help bond strands together and prevent moisture from evaporating. They are usually heavier than gels, mousses, and foams. Something marketed as a styling product is usually going to have a stronger hold than something marketed as a leave-in conditioner.

Gel stylers can be used to create casts around your curls or waves which add control and shine. A cast is the stiff feeling on the outside of the hair that sometimes forms before the hair is even fully dry. Some cream stylers also create a cast, but it is typically softer.

If you are using more than one styling product, you can distribute one and then the other or you can mix them together beforehand. When you mix your products together before you apply them, that is called "cocktailing". If you have two products that are creams or two products that are gels, you can cocktail them beforehand, making product-application faster. If you are going to use both a cream and a gel, layer them instead in order to avoid little white balls forming on the hair. This can also happen on your hands so be sure to wipe them off before switching from one type of product to the other.

PRODUCTS FOR VOLUME AND TEXTURE

Lightweight product is the most important factor in achieving bigger hair. Heavy products will make it impossible for curls to defy gravity or for waves to go wild. As we mentioned, conditioner adds weight to your hair. It also increases clumping of the hair. If you want maximum volume, you need to use products with minimum weight. If your hair is in good health, try skipping conditioner altogether. If it doesn't work out, you can supplement the lack of conditioner with a little bit of diluted cream styling product.

There are also styling products that create texture, so your hair does not feel as soft. These help with volume because it creates the second- or third-day "grit" on wash day. Salt sprays and texture sprays are popular options.

Ingredients that reduce moisture in styling products, such as short-chain alcohols, can suck up heavy water weight. This allows your strands to bounce up higher as they dry. Remember, not all hair has the same needs so not all hair should follow the same rules. Following the rules for hair that is prone to dryness when you have high-normal porosity hair could be significantly limiting your ability to see your curls or waves at their best.

WATER REMOVAL

After you have selected the styling product or products you are going to use, it is time to get your hair ready to apply the product. How much water you leave in your hair before applying product depends on what you want to achieve.

Less water is going to give you smaller formations, less weight, a stronger cast from your product, and more total hair volume (bigger hair). More water is going to give you larger formations, but less total hair volume and dilute the effect of your styling product (meaning you will need to use more in order to get a cast).

Hair that is not extremely dry can have some water removed before applying styling product. Some water removal techniques will create the least frizz from friction, but they also tend to remove less water from the hair.

Here is an easy guide to use for choosing what you use to remove water:

- **Hands:** least friction and least absorption
- **T-Shirt Material:** very little friction and medium absorption
- **Microfiber Towel:** little friction and more absorption
- **Terry Cloth Towel:** most friction and most absorption

We like to remove excess water by using a microfiber or t-shirt material towel to gently squeeze sections of hair starting from the root area and moving to the ends. You can also target the parts of your hair that hold the most excess water. We call this *spot-drying.*

If you are applying your styling product and realize you removed too much water, you can also spray it with a water bottle or turn the shower on for a moment to add water. We prefer to add water if needed than to use too much and end up over-diluting our styling products.

PLACING HAIR FOR STYLING

This is a technique we call *placing* and it helps make sure your strands have not wandered off to join with the wrong wave or curl formations and helps lift the hair off the scalp for root volume. After hand- or towel-drying and before putting styling product on your hands, rake your hands through your hair from scalp to ends at an elevation, creating a space between the hair and the scalp wherever you are raking. Rake out, not down - unless you want to vertically clump the hair together for elongation.

The easiest way to create elevation is to lean your head to the side you are raking. This will cause the layers on that side to separate vertically. If your hair is very tangled, you can use a small amount of styling product to help with slip.

CHAPTER 13: PRODUCT APPLICATION

After placing the hair, we distribute the styling product using our massaging technique that we discussed in Chapter 10. Next we rake and/or squeeze to create the wave or curl formations. Tilt your head to each side and rake outward to create separation and volume or keep your head upright and rake downward to cause *vertical clumping* which elongates curls and waves.

If you want to achieve different things in different areas of your hair then use multiple techniques. These are the styling product application techniques we use. They are in order from creating the smallest formations to creating the largest:

Raking
This technique encourages maximum separation. Create small gaps between your fingers. Stick your fingers into a section of hair, getting close to the scalp. Rake from roots to ends without squeezing your fingers together. The more times you rake through a section, the more you will break it up. Cup up the section to release weight if a tighter wave or curl is desired.

Raking + Squeezing
This technique creates small wave or curl formations. Create small gaps between your fingers. The smaller the gaps between your fingers, the smaller the curl or wave formations will be. Stick your fingers into a section of hair, getting close to the scalp. Gently squeeze your fingers together as you rake from roots to ends.

Peace-Fingers
This technique creates large horizontal wave or curl formations. Take a small sec-

tion of hair and fully smooth it out. Using the middle and pointer finger of one hand, pinch the area of the hair closest to the scalp. Continue pinching the section as you move through the ends. Catch the top of the section with the pointer finger of one hand and cup up the rest of the section with the other hand to release the weight of the hair so it can bounce up.

Palm-Squeezing

This technique will create the largest wave or curl formations and elongates waves and curls vertically. It is essentially the same as our massaging technique, explained in Chapter 10. Take a large section of hair. Fully smooth out the section. Wrap your hands around it, with your hands made into a fist shape. Squeeze from the scalp area all the way to the ends of the hair and release. If you want the hair to bounce up more, cup up the bottom of the section.

Styling Tip for Fine, Low Density Waves & Curls - Amber Pearson @amber.pearson.hair
"Fine hair has a tendency to stick to the scalp and this will decrease volume and can cause the scalp to show more. Make sure you get your roots lifted off your scalp first thing when you're setting up your style, whether that's on wash day or a restyle. Lean to each side and slide your hand into your hair, against your scalp, and gently jiggle your hair away from your scalp. If you have curls that like to coil back into themselves and sit on top of your head, it can create gaps in your style that reveal more of the scalp. You can gently pull them down or clip them down, over the low density area, to elongate them and create a fuller appearance. If you don't have enough time to diffuse until completely dry, at least get your root area for a few seconds to remove more water weight and start to set the root area of your style."

STYLING & DRYING TOOLS

Earlier in the book we discussed brushing and combing, but we will mention it here again, since a lot of people use tools to style their hair. If you are going to comb or brush your styling products through your hair, we suggest detangling first with your fingers to minimize breakage. Try to make only one pass through your hair with the brush or comb if you want to avoid damaging the cuticle.

Waves and curls are the most defined when all tangles are removed before bouncing up. This can be achieved using you a comb, brush or your fingers. As long as your hair is completely detangled first, using our *Peace-Fingers* or *Palm-Raking* technique will form smooth, shiny formations of waves or curls. Which you choose is up to you, but if you prioritize hair health over ease of styling, we would suggest using your hands as your styling tool.

Blow-dryers, diffusers, and hood dryers can enhance your style or simply make the drying process go by faster. If your blow-dryer is going to be used for both diffusing your waves or curls and occasionally smoothing out your hair, it is very important to get a professional-grade blow-dryer. Inexpensive dryers typically won't last as long, but more importantly, they pose a greater risk of overheating and potentially burning your hair.

Hood-dryers gently blow air from a hood that you place over your hair. Diffuser attachments create a soft, spread-out airflow, much like a hood-dryer does but on a much smaller scale. They literally "diffuse" the air from the blow-dryer. This creates a gentle, indirect source of warm air that helps speed up the drying process and can be used to enhance the volume of your hair using the techniques we will discuss later on.

CHAPTER 14: DRYING & RESTYLING

If you can not touch your hair while it is drying then you are forfeiting control over the result once you are finished applying your products. We say - *touch with intention*. When you know how to gently manipulate your hair while it dries you have a much better chance of achieving the style you want. These are our techniques:

"Shake-and-Separate" (Volume)
If you are air-drying, lean your head to each side and stick one hand in at the roots and shake. Do this a few times during the beginning of the air-drying process - while the hair is still wet. If you are diffusing, do the

same shake as you lean to each side and diffuse. Breaking up clumps while the hair is still wet or damp will help reduce the weight of each wave or curl so that it can shrink up more.

"Pinch-Stretch-Hover" (Length)

Once the cast has set on your hair, gently pinch the ends of a section of hair between your pointer and middle finger. Use the fingers of one hand to stretch your hair downward to the length you would like your hair to be and hover your diffuser over the section. For very tight coils, to avoid shrinking back up, try to get your hair completely dry before moving on to another section of hair.

"Cup-and-Hover" (Volume)

Cupping your hair up from the ends to your scalp while hovering your diffuser is a gentle way to fight gravity, encouraging curls or waves to dry in a tighter formation. This technique is most effective toward the end of your drying process because you want the hair to get completely dry and cooled off while in the cupped position. This will encourage the waves or curls to defy gravity. Even a tiny bit of water weight will drag the waves and curls back down.

AIR-DRYING AND DIFFUSING

Air-drying without touching your hair until it is completely dry will always give the most defined and controlled result. Be mindful that going out into a humid or dry climate, rain, snow, or wind before your hair is fully dry will increase the risk of losing definition.

Note: Low porosity hair can actually dry before water has a chance to absorb. This will cause pockets of water on the hair. A gentle press with a towel will absorb the pools of water.

You can use a diffuser to speed up the air-drying process by hovering it a few inches away from the hair. To add volume to your style, you can use our *cup-and-hover* technique. If you want maximum volume then begin cupping and diffusing right after applying styling products. If you want more control to your style but still some volume, air-drying until the cast is set on the outside of the hair and then using the cup-and-hover technique until completely dry will give you a combination of definition and volume. The cast is set when you can feel a slight stiffness on the outside of the hair but it still feels damp when you squeeze it.

Whether you choose to air-dry, diffuse, or combine techniques; keep in mind that your style is not set in place until your hair is completely dry *and* cooled off. Once the hair has cooled off, the bonds are temporarily set in their shape. Although gravity may cause your waves or curls to stretch, they will fight to stay in the formation they cooled off in.

RESTYLING

We suggest using a continuous spray bottle, which gives a light mist, to dampen your hair for restyling. If you want to create a stronger hold or add weight, you can dilute the styling product that is already in your hair with water and spray your hair with that. The water will cause the styling products already in your hair to resurface, so if you were happy with how much product you put in already, we recommend just using water.

After you spray your hair, gently massage the section you are restyling in order to help the moisture absorb. The strands of hair also need to be smoothed before they bounce up if you want to see defined waves or curls. The moisture from the water will allow your waves or curls to bounce back up so do not stress about running your hands through your hair. You can use one of our product application techniques to re-create your original style or switch it up. You can cup the hair up to the scalp if it needs bounce-assistance after smoothing and styling. The new cast should set much quicker than it did on wash day. You can then dry using your technique of choice.

BUILD YOUR OWN METHOD (B.Y.O.M.)

Now that you understand different techniques, you are ready to start designing your own looks. You can create one method that works great for you and use it every wash day or you can create a few different methods and understand what look each one will give you. Even better - you can just freestyle. If you are not there yet, give it some practice and soon styling will become a less conscious activity for you.

We hope you feel capable of coming up with your own styling methods now, but you still may learn other great things from bloggers and influencers online. When you watch a tutorial online, we suggest focusing more on the techniques and the product types than the specific brand of products used. If the person demonstrating the method is using a cream styler, you might be able to use a cream styler that you already have and know works great in your hair. This will save you from feeling like you need to buy new things every time you learn a new technique.

We created an example worksheet you can use to create and save your styling methods. It is frustrating when you find what works but forget what you did! Hopefully this will help.

B.Y.O.M. WORKSHEET

Desired Result: Definition & Volume
Product(s): Cream-based styler and gel
Tool(s): Blow-dryer and diffuser
Styling Prep: Squeeze from roots to ends with microfiber towel until hair is lightweight and only damp, place hair by raking from roots to ends at an elevation
Product Application: Apply cream massaged in followed by gel raked over top (don't forget to wipe hands between applications!), *Raking and Squeezing with Narrow Fingers* technique while tilted to the side being styled
Drying Technique: Immediately begin tilting head to each side, *cup-and-hover* technique on each side, repeat until dry, scrunch out any remaining cast

CHAPTER 15: SOCIAL MEDIA, SENSITIVITY, AND SELF-IMAGE

Social media can be a great tool to connect with other people who share our interests. However, with hundreds or even thousands of strangers interacting and sharing their opinions, there is bound to be disagreement. We face differing opinions in real life all the time, but it seems that on social media the level of sensitivity about hair styling and products is much higher.

We each harbor different emotions toward our hair and any negative past experiences

we have had because of it. This could con-
tribute to why we sometimes take offense
when we share something that works for
our hair and it doesn't work for someone
else. It is great to want to help others, but it
is not great to get upset with someone because what worked for you did not work for
them.

Misinterpretation is another major reason
social media arguments are so common. It
is very easy to misread something that is
written versus spoken. Facial expressions
and tone of voice play a huge role in the
way we interpret what someone says to us.
Both are taken away when we converse via
comments online. The only filter of inter-
pretation when comments are read online
is our own emotions. How we *feel* plays a
huge role in the voice we "hear" when we
read something.

If we feel vulnerable, we are probably going
to take something personal that may not
have been meant that way at all. Words can
really hurt and retaliation is easy from behind the safety of a screen. When engaged

in a discussion online, remember there is a person behind every thumbnail photo or account name. If you are feeling down or mad, try stepping away from the conversation until you feel better and coming back to it later.

Remember that you choose who you "hang out" with online. Social media communities can bring people together who share a common interest, hardship, or cause and that can be a great bonding or support system for people. However, if the communities you engage with online are making you feel bad or other people are being treated unfairly, ask yourself if this is a group of people you would want to spend time with in real life.

Harassment on social media can be as big as someone's picture being shared and people commenting horrible things on it or as small as someone responding aggressively to a difference in opinion. Either way, it hurts. Be gentle with others, but also be gentle with yourself by being mindful of what influences are around you online. If an

online community has a tendency to judge
or bully - you deserve better.

HOW TO LOVE YOUR HAIR EVERYDAY

Take compliments. When someone tells you something they like about you, it is because that is how they see you. Even if you do not see yourself in the same way they do, it is not necessary to let them know why the thing they complimented is not as great as they think it is. Maybe if we learn how to just say "thank you" when we receive compliments, we will get better at seeing ourselves the same way our admirers do.

Switch your focus. We tend to focus on the things we do not have instead of the things we do. We look at someone else's hair and see more volume or more length and meanwhile that same person may be looking back at us wishing for whatever it is our hair has that theirs does not. Take a little time to think about what you appreciate about your hair. You might be surprised how much you actually like about your own.

See beyond the screen. This is a big one. We are constantly comparing our real-life selves to *photos* of others. Remember that there is more than meets the eye when it comes to a photograph. Many social media beauty influencers are relentlessly placing all of their hair to one side to pose for a photo. They might push it all to the front or the back or maybe to one side of their face with their shoulder helping push the hair up. This is not reality. Do not wish you looked like that because even *they* do not look like that. As soon as the camera clicks and they take any motion, their hair will redistribute and the perfect angle, lighting and anti-gravity volume goes away. The people we admire photographs of are a lot closer to what we see in the mirror than you think.

CONCLUSION: MIRROR, MIRROR

Imagine there are two days of your life that you wake up looking exactly the same. One of those days you decide to take the time to "fix" your hair because you felt like you would not appear at a satisfactory level to yourself or others if you did not. You spend a little time restyling or a lot of time starting over completely with a new wash and go. On the other day, you wake up and you look at your hair, decide it is really not that bad, and leave it as is.

On the day you accepted your hair "as is", you likely woke up feeling more confident about other parts of yourself, inner or outer. You looked in the mirror and felt good and so your hair was also seen through that lens of self-confidence. Since you were not doing your hair, you had more time for yourself that morning. You left home feeling relaxed and content.

It is more likely you will receive praise for your hair (and probably other compliments as well) in the second scenario. The reason is that when other people look at you, they are not looking for the one thing that is not perfect, they are taking you in as a whole. Your positive mood and the fact that you have an air of confidence about you will affect the lens that others see you through. They will not notice frizz or limp curls; they will see a beautiful person shining all around.

So what do you actually look like when your hair is not perfect: the person you saw in the mirror in the first scenario that needed "fixing" or the person in the second scenario that does not need perfect hair to look and feel great? Can you possibly look like both at the same time? The reason that they say "beauty is in the eye of the beholder" is because it is really true.

How we feel about a person greatly impacts how we assess their physical appearance. It can often be a reflection of how we feel about ourselves as well. Maybe your friend does not like her eyes, but you perceive them as better than your own and so you think they are very beautiful. Beauty is relative and, for that reason, perfection is not based on a universal standard - it is based on the relationship between your mind and what you see in the mirror.

Have you ever loved someone so much that they were attractive to you no matter what condition they were in? We can love ourselves in that way. Perfection is not a physical destination; it is an emotional one. If we do our best to stop comparing and start supporting each other then we can all look at ourselves and see our own version of perfect. If this book has helped you in any small way to get closer to that destination - then it is an automatic success. Thank you for being a part of our journey as well.

ACKNOWLEDGEMENTS

Our family: Cathy Lieblich, Jessica Lieblich, Mark Lieblich, Phyllis Lieblich, Pilar Burgos, Ramon Mero and our fur-babies Maya and Shadow

In Loving Memory of
Severyn "Bernie" Lieblich

Scott Evans, Audio Engineer - For the creation of our audiobook. For business inquiries, email scottevans9@gmail.com.

Sabrina Gosnell & Michael O'Halloran, Extamus Media - For our amazing website (TheCurlNinjas.com). Check them out at Extamus.com.

Rachelle Vance, Portrait/Landscape Photographer - For our beautiful portraits for our website. Explore her work at RachelleVancePhotography.com.

Kelly Wilson, Nutrition Coach/Personal Trainer, FitFizz - For her contributions to the book.   Learn more at FitFizzStudio.com.

Felicia Slattery, Speaker/Consultant/Author - For her guidance on our self-publishing journey. Visit her website, FeliciaSlattery.com.

And to everyone who made donations to help support our efforts on social media and in making this book a reality:
Shannon Palmer, Joanna Riggs, Sarah Howell, Bronte Rodgers, Lori Shellenberger, Linda Tabach, Mick Davies, Taryn Foster, Suzanne Belmonte, Donna Schnack, Maria T Hannigan, Elisabeth Meier, Marie Miault, Patience Rudo Mlambo, Rebecca May-Cole, Fiona Stead, Rebekah Britton, Amrita Saylor, Susan Eckert, Freda Mclay, Debbie Lemire, Stephanie Wernz, Nahir Rosado, Natalie McCarthy, Suzanne Tassone, Emily Orlando, Hayley Burton, Kat Marquez, Nora Harper, Millie Robinson, Fi Baker, Hatishay Shawcroft, Lynn Melton, Destiney LaCoursiere, Jeneane Vespia, Zelly Rosa, Cristina Millett

ΔΔΔ

Didn't find the answer you were looking for? Email your question to crackingthecurlcode@gmail.com and like/follow our Facebook page "Cracking the Curl Code - The Epilogue" to see us post the question and answer to your questions and others!